JAMES SMITHSON
and the Smithsonian Story

JAMES SMITHSON

and the

SMITHSONIAN

STORY

By LEONARD CARMICHAEL

and J. C. LONG

G. P. PUTNAM'S SONS

With The Smithsonian Institution

NEW YORK

The original Star-Spangled Banner, fifty feet high, displayed in the center of the Museum of History and Technology. This is the flag which flew over Fort McHenry during the bombardment of Baltimore in the War of 1812 and inspired Francis Scott Key to write the words of what is now our National Anthem.

Second Impression

TO
S. DILLON RIPLEY

Zoologist, museum director, famed ornithologist,
international explorer of bird life in many countries,
writer of authentic works on natural history and

Eighth Secretary
of the
Smithsonian Institution

Contents

Part III. THE SMITHSONIAN'S BIRTH, GROWTH,
AND MODERN TIMES

PUBLISHER'S NOTE

The responsibility for the various sections of this book is divided among the authors as follows:

Leonard Carmichael, Seventh Secretary of the Smithsonian and Vice-President of the National Geographic Society, is the author of the opening chapters giving a general panorama of the history and development of the Smithsonian Institution.

J. C. Long, author of numerous biographies, especially in the Anglo-American field, is the author of the chapters depicting the life of James Smithson.

The third section, detailing the work of the various bureaus of the Smithsonian, is based on the documents and publications of the Smithsonian and is written by Long, who is responsible for the selection of the material.

PART I

OVERALL VIEW OF
THE SMITHSONIAN

CHAPTER 1

The Vision of James Smithson,
Made Real by Joseph Henry

Some things are said so well that they are worth quoting many times. This is true of Emerson's words, "An institution is the lengthened shadow of one man." Perhaps nowhere can this insight be more appropriately applied than to the modern Smithsonian Institution. This "shadow" of James Smithson the founder has now lengthened for more than one hundred and twenty years. It is a shadow, or here we might better say a light, that has been cast on the whole learned world. How and why Smithson's Institution started and has developed is the subject of this book.

Chief Justice Earl Warren, Chancellor of the Smithsonian, in his address delivered at the dedication and opening of the Smithsonian's new thirty-six-million-dollar Museum of History and Technology Building on January 22, 1964, said: "The Smithsonian Institution began as a dream in the mind of a solitary Englishman, an Oxford chemist of royal descent, who wondered how, after his death, his fortune might be applied to the advancement of learning and the benefit of all mankind." This, indeed, was a high ideal. Many men have dreamed dreams. Many have looked hopefully into the future. Not a few have given their fortunes for the advancement of scholarship and the betterment of their fellow men. But not many have been fortunate enough to have their objectives so faithfully carried out by the organization that their vision created. Perhaps in part this is because of the remarkable simplicity of the terms of the bequest. In his will Smithson simply said: "I bequeath the whole of my property . . . to the United States of America, to found at Washington, under the name of the Smithsonian Institution, an Establishment for the increase and diffusion of knowledge among men." Inherent in this clear direction was a healthy flexibility. The testament was firm and purposeful in its intent; yet it has allowed for growth as the decades have passed. But it has always imposed a heavy responsibility on all those who have been chosen to execute the requirements of the Smithson trust.

This responsibility has been felt and faithfully borne by each of the eight Secretaries who have directed the affairs of the Smithsonian. Each has lent his abilities, has projected his ideals and ideas, has applied his own peculiar interests and devotion. Each has led the Smithsonian into new paths of service. Each has been aware of and has been guided every day by the "lengthened shadow" of James Smithson.

If Smithson were alive today, would he be pleased by his institution?

Certainly he would be amazed. If by an "Establishment" he had in mind something on the order of the Royal Society of London or the Royal Institution, he would be surprised to find his institution a complex of buildings and bureaus, of art galleries and museums, of research laboratories and field stations. Being a mineralogist, he would be delighted to see the Smithsonian's great Hall of Gems and Minerals. He would probably smile with pleasure to see the beautiful specimens of the mineral smithsonite, which he first analyzed and which is named for him. He would be startled to discover that one of the branches of the Smithsonian now has as one of its greatest tasks in promoting the increase of knowledge the photographic tracking of artificial earth satellites which have been thrust by man into space. He would surely be gratified to know that over ten thousand publications bearing the name and seal of the Smithsonian Institution have been distributed by the million to every part of the earth and can be found in every great library of the world.

Yes, it is certain that Smithson would be pleased, for he was a man of ideas and of vision. Several years before the Institution was actually founded, and while its nature and administrative structure were still being debated in the halls of the United States Congress, John Quincy Adams, in a speech before the House of Representatives, said: "Of all the foundations of establishments for pious or charitable uses which ever signalized the spirit of the age or the comprehensive beneficence of the founder, none can be found more deserving the approbation of mankind than the Smithsonian Institution." The years have proved this encomium to be deserved. This statement is a tribute both to the clear wisdom of John Quincy Adams and to the daring originality of James Smithson.

The man most responsible for the early charting of the Smithsonian's course and keeping it on a right path was Joseph Henry. As the foremost American physicist of his day and probably the greatest American scientist since Franklin, he was a natural choice for the Smithsonian Board of Regents to make when they came, in 1846, to select the Institution's first chief administrator, or as he is called in good early American style, Secretary. It is difficult to imagine what the Smithsonian might have become had a lesser man been chosen. It is significant that Henry himself belonged in part to the age of Smithson (their lives overlapped by twenty-nine years). Henry's insight enabled him to sense the spirit and the intent of Smithson's bequest and to project the donor's idealism into the fabric of the Institution. He imposed on the Institution a sound and well-pondered plan of organization; and he was able to serve long enough (thirty-two years, until his death in 1878) to see it firmly established, his ideas bearing fruit, and the Smithsonian taking a secure place in the scientific and cultural life of the nation and building up a favorable place in the public mind. These early years were not all easy. Henry had his difficulties, as all dynamic pioneers do. But he was persistent, fair-minded, economical and conscientious; he had a plan for the Institution. A. Hunter Dupree has well stated in his book *Science in the Federal Government* that Henry's program for the Institution finally proved even more influential than the organic law of 1846 establishing the Smithsonian.

What were the principles on which Henry's master plan was founded?

First, Henry was realistic in realizing the limitations of the Institution's scope. He kept fighting off those who would have made it broad and thin. He well knew that the income from an endowment of $550,000 would go only so far. Although Smithson had placed no stipulations on the kinds or quantities of knowledge to be increased and diffused, Henry wisely saw the necessity of circumscription. Henry was a scientist; Smithson had been a scientist. And so it was natural that science would be the Smithsonian's forte. In this field Henry was sure of himself. Furthermore, the emphasis on science reflected the great need of America at that time. It is hard to remember how backward the United States was in what we call modern science when the Smithsonian was started. And in the years that have passed since Henry's day, whatever else the Smithsonian may have taken under its wing—art, history, museology, technology—science, and especially independent scientific research, has remained the strong backbone of its activities.

In some ways Henry thought of the Smithsonian in comprehensive terms. Smithson himself had said: "The man of science has no country; the world is his country, all men his countrymen." Therefore the Smithsonian Institution has been from the first international, not national or parochial. There should be nothing small-minded about it. To Henry and to Smithson there can be no doubt that "among men" meant all mankind. Knowledge was universal; the Smithsonian should keep its sights high and work for the increase of knowledge *per orbem* (as the Smithsonian Institution seal is inscribed). This was Henry's ideal, and in many ways he succeeded brilliantly.

Henry tried, too, to keep the Smithsonian free of politics or other influences that might tend to dilute its scholarly research activities. He was irked when political influence was exerted in an effort to obtain appointments. He resented the suggestion that science for political or other reasons must be immediately "practical"; for although he was not at all averse to what today we call applied science, he understood that the scientist whose objective is to discover first principles must be left unfettered. "He who loves truth for its own sake," he said, "feels that its highest claims are lowered and its moral influence marred by being continually summoned to the bar of immediate and palpable utility." And one of his objections to connecting the National Museum with the Smithsonian was that "it would annually bring the Institution before Congress as a supplicant for Government patronage."

Henry believed too that Smithsonian activities should be confined to those that it alone could carry on best. He was not an empire builder. When it came time for fledgling projects such as his own pioneering meteorological studies to leave the protection of the Smithsonian nest, he let them go willingly, believing that in this way science in the Government was being optimally served. There was no lack of things to do; there were many new paths to explore, as the never-ending quest for knowledge marched ahead. The Smithsonian had no need to compete with other institutions; rather, it would cooperate with them toward common ends. To make the most effective use of its limited income, it could best serve as a catalyst, encouraging and helping when most needed. A little aid at the right time could be the best possible kind. One illustrious example of this continuing Smithsonian tenet occurred many years later when the Institution made small grants from its own limited nongovernmental funds to Dr. Robert H. Goddard, at a critical time, in support of his experiments with rockets and thus helped him become the world's first scientific hero of the space age.

But above all, Henry laid down a pattern for the *increase* and *diffusion* of knowledge. He tried to interpret Smithson's words broadly but clearly. He kept the two concepts separate. "These though frequently confounded, are very different processes, and may exist independent of the other," he said. To increase knowledge he would use Smithsonian income to stimulate men of talent to do original research. He offered suitable rewards for memoirs containing new scientific discoveries. He appropriated annually funds for specific research projects. To diffuse knowledge the Smithsonian would carry on a program of publication and distribute these publications to scholars and institutions throughout the world. This it has done effectively ever since Henry's time.

There has never been any turning aside from Henry on these foundation stones on which he began building. Today, although the Smithsonian has expanded manyfold and in many directions, Henry's principles are still basic to its operations. They have always guided its destiny.

There was for a time grave doubt in Henry's mind as to the wisdom of attaching the federally supported United States National Museum to the Smithsonian. He said: "It could not be the intention of Congress that an Institution founded by the liberality of a foreigner, and to which he has affixed his name, should be charged with the keeping of a separate Museum, the property of the United States." But Congress—and others—disagreed.

CHAPTER 2

The Rise of the Museums

Henry's Assistant Secretary, Spencer Fullerton Baird (who succeeded him as Secretary in 1878), though never unloyal to his chief, was a devoted museum man. He lent his great knowledge as a biologist and his organizing abilities to building up the Museum collections, particularly in the field of natural history and in the products of technology. It was natural that in the development of the American nation there should be a national museum. Henry's objections were overridden, and the Museum was given to the Smithsonian to administer. This, too, Smithson would have approved. With the start of the Smithsonian's museum the proliferation of branches or bureaus of the Institution began. The fact that all but four of the twelve bureaus that make up the Smithsonian "family" today came after the Henry-Baird regimes is perhaps indicative of two influences: (1) the determination of Secretary Henry to keep the Smithsonian uncomplex and (2) the growing pressures from the American people as the years passed for services in the arts and sciences that the Smithsonian Institution seemed best qualified to provide.

Today the Smithsonian bureaus aggregate a multimillion-dollar establishment. They are supported partly by the income from private Smithsonian endowments, partly by gifts and grants, and partly from public funds annually appropriated by the Congress.

It might be difficult to explain to James Smithson how all this came about; and perhaps Joseph Henry would withhold his unqualified approval; but both would agree that the Smithsonian, in spite of its twentieth-century activity and bigness, is still faithful to the trust of increasing and diffusing knowledge among men. A brief review of its present finances may make this picture more vivid.

During the decade 1953–1963, the nonpublic invested funds (endowments) of the Smithsonian grew from about eleven million to over twenty-two million dollars. This is "book value." In market value these funds had a value in excess of twenty-five million at the end of the period. In this same decade over sixty-one millions were appropriated by the Congress to the Smithsonian for the planning and construction of buildings. In this decade the annual appropriations for operating funds for the bureaus of the Smithsonian grew from something under four and a half million to over seventeen million.

The oldest of the so-called bureaus of the Smithsonian is the United States National Museum. The National Museum did not spring full-flowered from the brow of Minerva. It had its roots in the desire of a young nation to preserve the records and artifacts of its history, culture, and achievements. Washington and Jefferson had advocated such an institution, and an organization called the National Institution for the Promotion of Science helped to carry out these objectives. Materials of the United States Exploring Expedition and the Lewis and Clark Expedition were assembled and in part put on display. There were a number of collections in government buildings, needing only an organization to gather the threads together. That function was assumed by the Smithsonian. It is interesting to remember that the authority for a museum was contained in the Smithsonian organic act of 1846, so that Congress, in spite of Henry's reluctance, wisely gave the museum an official place within the Smithsonian's sheltering arms. Under Baird's direction the museum soon outgrew its status as a "cabinet

Museum of History and Technology

of curiosities." In 1876, when sixty freight-car loads of exhibit material came from the closing Philadelphia Centennial Exposition, a new museum building was called for. This building became known as the Arts and Industries Building. But museum needs continued to grow, and just after the turn of the century the monumental Natural History Building was planned and erected. But growth did not stop there. Not only have two gigantic wings been recently added to the Natural History Building, but after many years of planning there was opened, early in 1964, the Smithsonian's great new Museum of History and Technology. Thus today, the United States National Museum, with its two branches—the Museum of Natural History and the Museum of History and Technology—both supported by annual appropriations from Federal funds, is the largest bureau of the Smithsonian. In total, this museum is now indeed probably the largest museum complex in the world. Its collections include some fifty-eight million catalogued objects. It is an important agency in the scientific research activity and the educational life of our country.

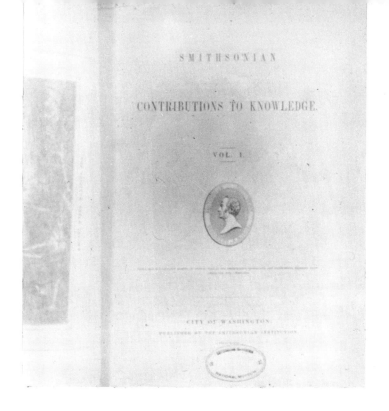

Title page of the first publication of the Smithsonian, issued in 1847

International Exchange Service

In 1848, the Smithsonian issued its first scientific publication, a classic in the then very new field of American archaeology—*Ancient Monuments of the Mississippi Valley,** by E. G. Squier, M.A. and E. H. Davis, M.D. In the process of seeking a mechanism to achieve an optimum worldwide distribution of this book, Secretary Henry devised a scheme which gradually developed into a permanent service for the international exchange of scientific and literary publications. It is still very much in operation. The manner in which it operates is relatively simple. Libraries, scientific societies, educational institutions, and individuals, in this country, who wish to distribute their publications abroad as gifts or exchanges, send the separately addressed packages to the Smithsonian, carriage cost prepaid. There they are sorted by countries

* This book is frequently catalogued under the title *Smithsonian Contributions to Knowledge,* Vol 1.

and forwarded with similar shipments from other organizations to exchange agencies in other parts of the world, where they are distributed to the addressees. Similarly, shipments of publications from exchange agencies abroad to the Smithsonian are distributed free to addressees in the United States. The plan has worked extremely well. For the most part it is now conducted under more than fifty treaty agreements with foreign countries, and since 1881 the costs of this series have been underwritten by the Federal Government. As one commentator has said, "The Exchange Service has demonstrated itself as a very tangible expression of the Smithsonian Institution's part in 'the diffusion of knowledge.' It, again, is an instance of that cooperative kind of enterprise envisioned by Joseph Henry as the most effective means for the Smithsonian to fulfill its purpose."

Bureau of American Ethnology

The scientific study of man was a very early concern of the Smithsonian. As we have said, the first publication of the Institution was a monograph on the prehistoric relics and mounds of the aborigines of the Mississippi Valley. In his Report for 1870 Henry remarked: "The collection of objects to illustrate anthropology now in the possession of the Institution is almost unsurpassed, especially those which relate to the present Indians and the more ancient inhabitants of the American continent." And seven years later, in his last Annual Report, he said: "Anthropology, or what may be considered the natural history of man, is at present the most popular branch of science." The Smithsonian through these years became a leader in this science, and it was natural that eventually its anthropological interests should be corralled and centralized. This came about in 1879 under the dynamic inspiration and leadership of a most remarkable man, Major John Wesley Powell. He was the hero of the Colorado River explorations and an eminent geologist. When the Bureau of Ethnology (the name was later changed to the Bureau of American Ethnology) was established by sanction of Congress as a branch of the Smithsonian, Powell became the first Chief of the Bureau. Though never large in personnel, the Bureau waxed strong in prestige and leadership. It began publishing a distinguished series of reports and bulletins based on its researches, on the languages, customs, religion, and remains of the American Indians. This work has gone on for eighty-five years, and as we look back over the history of this bureau we cannot help being impressed by the luster it has added to the Smithsonian. It has been one of the most felicitous of Smithsonian undertakings in *both* the increase and the diffusion of knowledge. As a result of the work of this organization the world has a permanent scientific understanding of the various activities of the New Stone Age human beings who once alone inhabited this entire hemisphere.

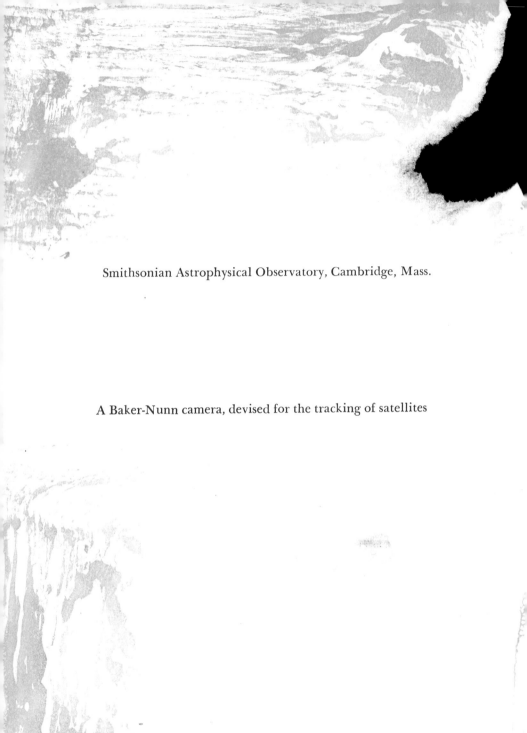

Smithsonian Astrophysical Observatory, Cambridge, Mass.

A Baker-Nunn camera, devised for the tracking of satellites

CHAPTER 3

Aviation and Celestial Studies
under Langley

The Astrophysical Observatory

Following the death of Baird in 1887, Samuel Pierpont Langley became the Smithsonian's third Secretary. He was already a great astronomer and experimental technician, and he left his mark on the Smithsonian in many ways, the chief of which perhaps was the manner in which he led astronomy out of its traditional patterns into what he called the "new astronomy." Its principal concern was the study of the sun, and in 1890 the "new astronomy" found a home in a new bureau of the Smithsonian: the Astrophysical Observatory. The purpose was not only that of the usual observatory, "to study the places and motions of the heavenly bodies," but also, as Langley put it, to discover how the sun "affects the earth and the wants of man on it: how its heat is distributed, and how it, in fact, affects not only the seasons and the farmer's crops, but the whole system of living things on the earth." This basic objective, firmly established by Langley, has been adhered to, and many important discoveries have been made by the Observatory's scientists. In recent years its work has greatly broadened and its scientific headquarters have been removed to Cambridge, Massachusetts, where, in close cooperation with the Harvard College Observatory, it carries on research in which physics, chemistry, and mathematics are all used in the service of a still "newer" astronomy which employs artificial satellites as its tools and as orbiting observing stations. Here a new solar science, lunar science, meteoritical science, and the visual tracking of artificial earth satellites are all advanced. The Division of Radiation and Organisms is part of the astrophysical work of the Smithsonian and is in Washington. It carries on a great variety of studies of the influences of radiation on plant and animal life, the secrets of photosynthesis,* and other basic investigations. Much of this very modern work has its roots in concepts propounded with so much brilliance by Samuel P. Langley.

* The process by which sunlight acting on the leaves of plants results in chlorophyll-containing tissues.

CHAPTER 4

Beginnings of a Scientific Zoo and the Consolidating Works of Walcott and Abbot

The National Zoological Park

Most Smithsonian programs have begun modestly; there has been left plenty of room to grow. Especially was this true of the National Zoological Park, a second Smithsonian bureau that had its inception with Dr. Langley. He was among those who saw the need for such a "zoological garden" for the nation. He helped promote it before Congress. He selected its site on Washington's Rock Creek for its home. Langley's selection of this site had much to do with the later setting aside of Rock Creek as Washington's great green recreational haven. One of Langley's objectives in establishing the Zoological Park was to bring to the attention of the American people the necessity of preserving the country's dwindling species of big game animals, particularly the bison. He saw that the long-term need was one of education and research. The Park, officially established in 1890, provided a place where the many visitors to Washington could become acquainted with and learn to appreciate the wild animals—our co-dwellers on this earth—and also where scientists could study them and learn more about their forms and habits. In all these objectives the national zoo has been an eminent success, and from a small herd of bison originally quartered in a paddock behind the Smithsonian Building, the National Zoological Park has grown to be one of the largest and best zoos in the world. The relationship between the distinguished staff in scientific zoology at the Natural History Museum and the staff at the Zoo has always been close and fruitful. The fact that the Museum has experts on birds, mammals, reptiles and other forms has given the Zoo a scientific basis which would be very expensive were not both units under the same Smithsonian administration. The Zoo is, of course, a means of diffusing zoological knowledge as well as constructive recreation to millions of persons each year.

Paul H. Oehser in his excellent book *Sons of Science* says that it has been generally considered that the Secretaryship of the Smithsonian is the greatest honor that can come to an American man of science. Certainly the man who was the fourth Secretary, Charles Doolittle Walcott, was already world-famous when he came to the Smithsonian as Dr. Langley's successor. He served from 1907 to 1927. When he was chosen, he was Director of the United States Geological Survey and recognized everywhere as a great authority in paleontology. Dr. Walcott was influential in the establishment of the Carnegie Institution of Washington, the National Advisory Committee for Aeronautics and the Research Corporation. With these three organizations the Smithsonian has had close association.

In Dr. Walcott's Secretaryship the Natural History Building of the Smithsonian was completed and many advances made in the scientific research programs of the Institution.

Charles Greeley Abbot, one of America's greatest astrophysicists, succeeded Walcott and became the fifth Secretary of the Smithsonian. He served as Secretary from 1928 to 1944. Dr. Abbot's life has been devoted to science. He completed the mapping of the infrared solar spectrum begun by Dr. Langley and studied variations in solar radiation, especially in relation to weather variation and plant life. During his Secretaryship substantial additions were made to the invested funds of the Institution and many improvements were made at the National Zoological Park and in the Bureau of American Ethnology.

The Art Galleries

It is not sure that Smithson ever dreamed that his institution would one day encompass not only the largest museum complex in the world but also one of the greatest art centers. But the protective arms of the Smithsonian today embrace four art galleries. This too has been a logical development, for from the very beginning the Smithsonian began to accumulate objects of art, and a "gallery of art" was provided for in the organic act establishing the Institution. It was not until Langley's time, however, that *ars smithsoniana* began to crystallize. In 1906, through an interesting set of circumstances, the Smithsonian art collection became officially recognized as an integral part of the Institution. The *pièce de résistance* of this gallery was a collection of paintings given some years before by President Buchanan's niece, Harriet Lane Johnston. This part of the Institution became known as the National Collection of Fine Arts.

Soon the Gallery began to attract other donations, notably that of the Detroit industrialist, Charles Lang Freer, who in 1906 offered his entire Oriental and American art collection to the Smithsonian and a building to house it. This became a separate branch—the Freer Gallery of Art—and today it is one of the most splendid and precious of Smithsonian possessions. It has been called "the jewel in the Smithsonian's crown." And then, on December 31, 1935, Andrew Mellon gave to the American people his art collection, a $15,000,000 building to exhibit it, and a generous endowment fund. This very great gallery is a bureau of the Smithsonian Institution but it is administered by its own board of trustees. It is known as the National Gallery of Art.

Congress established in 1962 the National Portrait Gallery as a bureau of the Smithsonian for "the exhibition and study of portraiture and statuary depicting men and women who have made

National Gallery of Art

Freer Gallery of Art

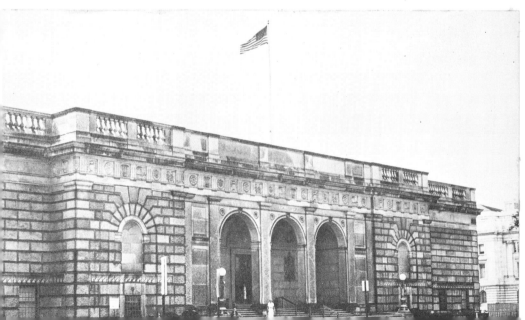

significant contributions to the history, development, and culture of the people of the United States and of the artists who created such portraiture and statuary." Both the National Collection of Fine Arts and the National Portrait Gallery are accorded excellent and ample quarters in the old Patent Office Building, renovated for this purpose. Art at the Smithsonian surely has a great future, supported by a firm foundation well laid by private philanthropy and federal generosity.

The Air and Space Museum

The Smithsonian's interest in aeronautics, although in fact dating from the time of Joseph Henry who encouraged the balloon experiments of Thaddeus Lowe during the Civil War, received its initial great impetus from Secretary Langley, whose experiments with heavier-than-air craft brought fame to him as well as identifying the Smithsonian with pioneering aviation. Regardless of the fact that his man-carrying aerodrome plunged into the Potomac a few days before the Wright Brothers' success at Kitty Hawk, Langley made significant and lasting contributions to the science of aeronautics. The letter from Wilbur Wright asking the Smithsonian for suggestions as to how to begin experiments on human flight is still preserved at the Institution.

The Smithsonian, under Langley's aegis, began to collect the artifacts of aviation, which now have been increased and enhanced until the Smithsonian aeronautical collections have no equal. For many years a part of the engineering division in the United States National Museum, the aeronautical collection achieved separate status in 1946 when Congress established the National Air Museum as a bureau of the Smithsonian. This museum is entering a new era. Funds to plan a monumental new building on the Mall in Washington have been appropriated by the Congress. This Smithsonian bureau is surely destined to play a growing and magnificent role in memorializing America's achievements in aviation and in the conquest of space.

CHAPTER 5

Recent Developments
and Future Prospects

Canal Zone Biological Area

In 1946 Alexander Wetmore, the sixth Secretary of the Smithsonian and a most distinguished scientific student of living and fossil birds and of avian behavior, was responsible for adding another unit to the Smithsonian complex. This involved the guardianship and administration of a six-mile-square island wilderness in the middle of Gatun Lake in Panama—Barro Colorado Island. The island was formed years ago when a dam was built across the Chagres River to form a lake. The result was an unspoiled habitat for tropical fauna and flora, and scientists seized the opportunity to preserve the island for purposes of biological research. And so it has remained—the only tropical scientific research station of its kind in the New World. Here facilities are maintained to accommodate serious students of all kinds—zoologists, ecologists, entomologists, ornithologists, botanists, also photographers—who want to investigate the unusual life of this primitive area. Nowhere else can one find the exact conditions, habitat, and habitants that make scientific study here so valuable. Nowhere else is exactly the kind of research that can be carried on here possible.

Barro Colorado Island, in the middle of Gatun Lake, Canal Zone, where tropical research is done by the Smithsonian Institution

Over a thousand scientific reports have been published on research done at this station of the Smithsonian.

The Kennedy Center

The National Cultural Center (in 1964 renamed the John F. Kennedy Center for the Performing Arts) was established as a bureau of the Smithsonian by Congress in 1958. Like the National Gallery of Art, it is administered by a separate board of trustees. Its purpose is to provide facilities and encouragement for the performing arts in the nation's capital. Congress provided a magnificent site for the Center on the shores of the Potomac. Construction funds are being raised by voluntary contributions of the American people, matched by a Federal appropriation of fifteen and a half million dollars. Many substantial private donations have already been made. The Kennedy Center is a significant evidence of the trend in the United States toward greater support for and participation in not only the sciences but also the arts. The immediate beneficiaries of the Kennedy Center will be the people of every state in the Union, as the influence of the Center spreads. Its programs will proliferate and it will attract artistic talent from all over the world. It is also an educational enterprise. Some may have wondered why the Center is attached to the Smithsonian. Perhaps the reason is that the Smithsonian has become an American equivalent of the ministries of culture which have been established in so many European nations. The American people are continually expecting more of the Smithsonian. They have learned to believe in it and to depend on its competence and its disinterested service for science, the arts, and education.

Leonard Carmichael served as the seventh Secretary of the Smithsonian Institution, from 1952–1964. During these years special emphasis was given to the development and support of the research activities of the Institution and to making the Smithsonian more broadly recognized as one of the great scientific teaching centers, at the postgraduate level, in America. During this period the new Museum of History and Technology Building of the Smithsonian was built with appropriations totaling thirty-six million dollars. New wings and total air-conditioning for the Museum of Natural History were provided, for twenty-million dollars. The old Patent Office Building was transferred to the Smithsonian, with nine million dollars for its reconstruction. Planning money of over two million dollars was approved for the new Air Museum of the Institution, and the first appropriations were made to start the approved seventeen million dollar reconstruction of the National Zoological Park.

Dr. S. Dillon Ripley, became the eighth Secretary on February 1, 1964. Before coming to Washington he had served at Yale University with outstanding distinction as a zoology professor and as head of the Peabody Museum. He has begun new educational and international programs and has initiated important scientific and other types of work at the Smithsonian. Certainly the Institution under his dynamic leadership is today an active and fruitful center

for the welfare not only of all Americans but of mankind everywhere.

Many have suggested that the bureaus of the Smithsonian are
separate entities. Actually, all parts of the Institution are closely
associated and each gains strength from the others. One common

Hall of Health, de-
voted to "man's
knowledge of his
body, then and now"

service of the Institution is its publication program. As already
noted, from the start, and down through the administrations of all
eight Secretaries, the Smithsonian's publications have formed the
bulwark of its function in the "diffusion of knowledge." Smithsonian publications are known the world over. They are in every
important library everywhere. The Smithsonian imprint has ap-

peared on at least ten thousand titles, ranging from small pamphlets to multivolume books, in all branches of the sciences and the arts. An estimated total of twelve million copies and unit publications have been distributed.

Another function of vast importance that has loomed large in the Institution's history is its work in exploration. The development of field studies is not confined to one bureau but is emphasized throughout the whole Institution. Smithsonian expeditions have covered the earth like a gigantic net. The amount of scientific information that has resulted is truly incalculable. The Smithsonian Library, which has been invaluable to Smithsonian scientists since the beginning of the Institution's history, has in its working collection some of the largest and most useful specialized libraries of scientific literature in the world.

It is thus clear that it is not simple to describe the Institution that resulted from the dream and the act of James Smithson. One question remains: Where will it all end? Will the Smithsonian continue to grow bigger and bigger, with more buildings, more functions, more staff? All the evidence of the past suggests that this will indeed be the case. It seems almost certain that as long as America remains, the Smithsonian will continue because of the nature of its genesis and the wisdom of its organizers and the unique character of its services for the welfare of America. The Smithsonian is greater than the sum of its parts. If—by any stretch of the imagination—its present twelve "bureaus" should be translated to the moon, the Smithsonian's foundation would remain, and new fields of service and new ways to "increase and diffuse knowledge" would arise like the phoenix bird. The old foundation is firm. No one knows, in the present accelerating pace of science, technology, and the arts, what the opportunities and exigencies of the future will provide. James Smithson said that his ambition as a scientist was "to enlarge the lurid specks in the vast field of darkness." Somehow, paradoxically, as knowledge increases, the field of darkness is seen as ever larger too. For every victory that science wins, it opens a hundred more campaigns that need to be prosecuted. We can only hope each year to enlarge the specks of light as we go along. This is a never-ending quest and challenge. This book tells the story of how the Smithsonian came to be, how it has met its challenges, and some idea of the problems of the future which it must face and solve as it has during the more than a century of sturdy growth.

PART II

THE LIFE OF JAMES SMITHSON

(1765–1829)

FOUNDER OF THE SMITHSONIAN INSTITUTION

All of the papers of James Smithson were brought to the United States in the early 1800's and ultimately housed in the newly established Smithsonian Institution.

In 1865, they were destroyed by a fire except for a few items lodged elsewhere. As Smithson had neither wife nor children nor any close relatives, there was no easily accessible source for the facts of his personal life.

In the following chapters are presented for the first time the gist of certain major documents relative to Smithson, such as his mother's will; his British naturalization paper (he was born in Paris); a proviso by the Crown that he could never hold high office; his sufferings as a prisoner of war; financial data of himself and his mother at the Hoare Bank; the disputed circumstances of his brother's birth; his experiences in France and other countries on the Continent; his official warrant to use the name of Smithson; and highlights of his scientific career.

Rhees, Langley, and Oehser have written important biographical sketches. Rhees, when chief clerk of the Smithsonian, wrote the pioneer work in 1879 which summarized the data available in the United States, such as the text of Smithson's published papers. S. P. Langley, Secretary of the Smithsonian, went abroad in 1894 and gathered at firsthand information regarding Smithson's education at Pembroke College, Oxford, where he had been entered under the name of James Macie. Both Rhees and Langley filled in some blanks in the Smithson story with certain surmises which ultimately proved to be in error.

The most reliable biographical summary of Smithson is that of Paul H. Oehser in Sons of Science. *He includes data from Rhees and Langley without repeating their errors, and adds various items of interest.*

The Dictionary of National Biography (*British*), *though providing a generally useful summary, makes some curious mistakes. It gives the name of Smithson's mother's husband as* James Macie, *whereas the marriage certificate and other data have* John Macie. *It asserts unequivocally that the mother had a husband prior to Macie and that her second son was the result of that supposed marriage. However, proof of that marriage is lacking and the second son was far too young to have been an offspring of that union.*

Even though the Smithson personal files were destroyed by fire, the ramifications of his life have become known through various sources—the Public Record Office, wills on file in Somerset House, consular reports from countries which he visited, letters from him in manuscript collections of his contemporaries, comments about him in the writings of his fellow scientists, and personal visits to those countries which he explored.

Readers should regard as fiction a book published in 1934 under the title of Wing of Fame *by Louise W. Hackney, a novel with the subtitle:* Based on the Life of James Smithson. *In contrast to some historical novels which are based on careful research, this work is quite fanciful. It invents various scenes and incidents, and even provides Smithson with an American wife.*

CHAPTER 1

The Young Scientists

James Lewis Macie Smithson, an identifier of zinc oxide, classifier of calamines, was founder of the Smithsonian Institution in Washington, D.C.

He was one of that coterie of young scientists who burst upon the world in the late eighteenth century bringing the wonders of the earth and sky to the service of man.

Volta, Ampère, Galvani, Ohm, Watt—their works brought new words to the dictionary. Such was the word "smithsonite" which connoted a whole new complex of zinc applications.

For it was Smithson who discovered deposits of special zinc ores in Somersetshire and Derbyshire, England, and recognized their differences. He classified the related calamines; and his paper on the subject, read before the Royal Society in 1802, was a landmark in the progress of applied science.

Smithson did not limit his discoveries to zinc or to other aspects of the physical world. He and the other young scientists chose the universe as their laboratory. Priestley, Blagden, Klaproth, Gilbert, Fabbroni, Cavendish, Banks, Arago, Davy, Lamarck, Cuvier: Smithson knew most of them personally, and they regarded him as their peer.

Smithson had more than his share of obstacles: the circumstances of his birth, the bohemian atmosphere of his home life, the official edict which barred him from any Government honors; yet he surmounted all that would have destroyed a lesser man and at the end won a fame that will endure in perpetuity.

CHAPTER 2

Wife of Bath

In 1761, Mrs. Elizabeth Hungerford Keate Macie, who was to become the mother of James Smithson, founder of the Smithsonian Institution, was enjoying the freedom of widowhood and the elaborate social life of Bath, which in that period was the favorite playground of England for the upper classes. Here Queen Charlotte (the wife of George III), princes of the blood, dukes, earls, and minor lords could cavort without the restrictions of court etiquette.

Bath, only slightly over a hundred miles from London, had been founded by the Romans during their occupation and had been in use intermittently ever since. The location abounded in natural springs—hot springs, cold springs, sulphur springs, saline springs. It had all the facilities for a health resort. The Romans, with their engineering genius, had built a major bath pool (still in operation) and numerous auxiliary springs.

Although under the series of struggles which followed the Norman conquest, Bath fell into disuse as a social center, by the time of Queen Elizabeth I, the resort had been restored to some extent. Her Majesty visited there, but was disturbed by the fact that a certain hot bath scalded her epidermis; whereupon she established a more tepid pool, known as the Queen's Bath.

The place by 1761 was democratic with the democracy of dollars. Anyone who had the money was welcome. When William Pitt, the later Lord Chatham, bought his house in The Circle at Bath, his favorite crony was Ralph Allen, an erstwhile local bartender with a gift for real estate promotion. Allen had become one of the wealthiest men in England and had built himself an elaborate residential park.

The widow Macie had both money and youth. She was in her early thirties, which was young for that sophisticated society. Her money came from several sources. She was an heiress of the Hungerford estates. She was a direct descendant of Sir George Hungerford, founder of the vast Hungerford properties and husband of Lady Frances Seymour. They had a daughter, Frances, who married John Keate.

That couple gave birth to another John Keate, a captain in the Scotch Horse Grenadiers. He married Penelope Fleming. From this union were born Lumley Hungerford Keate and his sister Elizabeth, Smithson's mother-to-be. She had inherited only a portion of the Hungerford fortunes at this time though later the estates of her brother and other relatives were willed to her. The ultimate value of the Hungerford properties may be gauged by the fact that Elizabeth's small share in the sale of one of them, Hungerford Manor, amounted to eleven thousand pounds, and her accumulated wealth through the years, most of which went to her son, James, has been estimated at around one hundred thousand pounds.

At this time, she had been left in comfortable circumstances by her late husband, John Macie. He had died at the age of forty-one having had no children, but evidently still hoping for an heir, because his will referred repeatedly to the possibility that if his wife became "enceinte" then certain properties should be held for his heir. As it was, he left Elizabeth several hundred pounds cash, their substantial homestead in suburban Weston, the silver, linen, and other household chattels, and other real estate properties. He also left her a good name, for he was High Sheriff of the County and an official in the Cathedral Church. Today there is a plaque to his memory on the left wall of the chancel, complete with data about his life and his coat of arms.

Since the husband had been so eminent in the area, there has been conjecture as to why neither Elizabeth's marriage certificate nor birth record were entered in the county archives—if she were a native of that region. The explanation is that Elizabeth Keate was a London girl, from a fashionable section of Middlesex (where Horace Walpole had a town residence) and where an Edward Macie also resided. Conceivably he was a relative who introduced John to Elizabeth. In any case the two were married in 1750, in Saint Paul's Cathedral. The marriage register of Saint Paul's has the following entry:

John Macie of Weston, in the County of Somerset, bachelor, and Elizabeth Keate, of the parish of St. Margaret, Westminster, in the County of Middlesex, spinster were married by Licence in this Cathedral on the 28th day of August 1750 by me W. Alsop, rector of Langridge, Somerset. Present: Benjamin Pearce, Sacrist.

Elizabeth seemed to be a pillar of society, though she reminds one of Chaucer's Wife of Bath, for it was said without clear proof that she had several husbands with or without benefit of clergy. She proved to be a prudent and orderly manager of her properties, but much of her romantic life is a mystery. Supposedly she had had a marriage—previous to becoming Mrs. Macie—to a certain Mark Dickenson. That name appears in a pedigree of the Hungerford family drawn up by a Rev. Frederick Brown in 1878 and currently on file in the British Museum. The pedigree notes that the Dickenson marriage was "dissolved" but the whole report may be an error, as Mr. Brown was capable of error. For example, he lists Elizabeth's husband as James Macie whereas the name of *John* and his marriage to Elizabeth is fully documented.

The suspicion of irregular behavior was not injurious to one's reputation in the society of Bath so long as appearances were maintained. In fact, a great store was set by appearances. The community accepted the unofficial rule of Beau Nash who established the code for the Pump Room and other social centers in Bath. The history of Nash is comparable to the leadership requirements in international society in any era. He moved into a social vacuum, into a group of individuals associated by chance, like the guests of a resort hotel. They needed a social director and arbiter.

Early in the Eighteenth Century, Nash became Master of Ceremonies at Bath and remained in that post for nearly sixty years. The post was informal, possibly created by Nash himself. No salary was attached. There was no board of directors. Nash subsisted mostly by his skill at cards. When that failed, infrequently, friends came to the rescue. Though personally he was a wastrel, his governing was on a high moral plane. Ladies and gentlemen must abide by certain standards of dress and decorum. The virtue of women, especially young women, was protected; in going to and from the public assembly rooms they must have reputable escorts.

Elizabeth Macie had status. She was a descendant of kings, specifically Henry VII, through the line of the Duke of Somerset. She was also related to the Percys, one of England's most noted families. A certain Percy, cousin to Elizabeth, was Lady Hugh Smithson, wife of Sir Hugh Smithson. The latter was due to inherit several titles from his wife's father including the earldom of Northumberland which ultimately devolved upon Sir Hugh. His promotion from that eminence to a dukedom was due apparently to his own abilities and his service to the Crown.

However, Sir Hugh was born a commoner. There was not a drop of noble blood in his system; but he had a gift for acquisition. He was not born a Percy but he became a Percy by act of Parliament. When he married, his wife's estates were impoverished, but in due course he made them prosper. Sir Hugh was in his forties when he took a holiday at Bath. He was a handsome man with drive and social graces; immediately he was a popular figure. Horace Walpole, the noted raconteur, frequented Bath and remarked on the physical beauty of Sir Hugh.

Sir Hugh's appeal to women may be illustrated by an anecdote

Hugh Smithson, First Duke of Northumberland, father of James Smithson

attributed to his wife. It seems that Sir Hugh had proposed to someone and had been rejected. When his future wife heard of it she said that she did not see how any woman could refuse so attractive a man; and of course the remark was carried back to Sir Hugh with the intended result.

Sir Hugh's meeting with Elizabeth was inevitable in view of their cousinship, in fact quite probably he knew her before coming to Bath. The affair between Elizabeth and Sir Hugh proceeded apace until 1764, when she discovered to her horror that she was "enceinte." The cardinal sin in Bath as in many societies was in getting caught. Elizabeth fled from Bath to Paris, never to return. In due course she obliterated every trace of her name in the Bath community, selling her properties or transferring them to agents. No record of her existence can be found in the archives of that county today. In Paris, in 1765, she gave birth to a son who was known until the age of thirty-six as James Macie. His name was changed to Smithson by the assent of the Crown in 1801.

Meanwhile Elizabeth built herself a new life in Paris and in London leading a publicly sedate existence until she died in 1800.

Note: W. J. Rhees, author of *James Smithson and His Bequest* was the first historian of Smithson, writing in 1879. Rhees was a chief clerk of the Smithsonian and did amazingly well with the materials that were available to him. Unfortunately he made certain errors, which occasionally have been copied by later writers. For example he gives the birth date of James as 1754, says that the place of his nativity is "unknown" and as to the mother "nothing has been learned of her history."

CHAPTER 3

On Becoming a British Subject

Mrs. Elizabeth Macie left no record of her residence in France or the birth of her son James.

There is no mention of her in any connection in the National Archives of France. Apparently she did not report to the British Consulate. The Consular dispatches of 1765 and adjacent years were sent to the Foreign Office in London and are on file in the Public Record Office. Her name does not appear. Unless she registered under an alias, an Elizabeth Macie and the birth of a child should have been in the Police records either of the municipality or of the arrondissement in which she was living.

The Germans however took possession of numerous public records first in 1870 and again in World War II. In the second instance they removed thousands of items from the files, carting them away to Germany. Conceivably they might be useful to the "Master Race" in providing detailed information about the conquered people. Hence any public trace of Elizabeth may have been in the purloined data.

Though Mrs. Macie and her late husband were staunch adherents of the Church of England she apparently did not affiliate herself with the small British colony in France. There was no formal church organization in Paris at that time, though services were held in the Embassy. The office of the Bishop of Fulham has jurisdiction over the Paris congregation but there is no record in that office of the existence of Elizabeth Macie. Further, the Huguenots compiled a directory of Protestants in the Capital but there is no mention of Mrs. Macie.

There may have been a cogent reason for this apparent concealment and for keeping the secret indefinitely, even after her son, James, had grown to maturity. The babe may have started life as a Roman Catholic. If Elizabeth had given birth in a French hospital, or if the accouchement had been supervised by nuns, the infant would have been immediately baptized by a Roman Catholic priest with or without the mother's consent. The Catholic issue in England was acutely political at this time. The Roman Church was identified with the government of France. The royal family in England had reason to fear an invasion under the leadership of a Pretender supported by France.

When Elizabeth arranged for her son to make application to be naturalized as a British subject the petition stated at the outset that the boy was "born at Paris but educated in the Protestant religion." James was approaching ten years of age when this petition was presented to the Crown.

Elizabeth conceivably could have raised the boy on the Continent where he could have lived in obscurity and she herself could have been forgotten. She had the financial resources to mingle in international society, but her loyalty was intensively British and she desired a distinguished career for James. Step by step she took every means within her power to assure him a worthy future.

Hence she arranged for his residence in England at the time of the petition. She put him under the legal guardianship of a Joseph Gape of the Inner Temple. (Gape was a trustee of the Hungerford estates and hence known to Elizabeth.) Gape accordingly was the attorney who presented the petition. The address of James was stated to be in the parish of St. Mary leBow in the County of Middlesex, which was in the heart of the City. His age was given as "nine years and four months or thereabouts." The omission of an exact birth date was peculiar, and presumably Elizabeth wished it so.

The boy's name appears in the document "Jacques otherwise James Louis."

The petition was granted by the Crown, in considerable detail, though with a proviso. The authorization said "James Louis shall be and is hereby from henceforth naturalized and shall be adjudged and taken to all intents and purposes to be naturalized and a free born subject of this Kingdom of Great Britain." It continued to detail the privileges such as the right to inherit property, the right to own manors, lands, goods, chattels, estates and to have all other privileges, immunities, benefits, and advantages in law or in equity.

The statement appeared to cover every advantage to which a British subject was entitled but it was followed by a curious proviso which declared "that the said Jacques otherwise James Louis *shall not be hereby enabled to be of the Privy Council or a member of either House of Parliament or to take any office or place of trust either civil or military or to have any grant of lands, tenements or hereditaments any inheritable property from the Crown to him or to any person or persons in trust for him anything herein contained to the contrary not withstanding.*"

The limitations imposed by this naturalization document were most extraordinary. There was nothing in basic law which decreed that illegitimate birth, as such, would deprive a subject of the various opportunities and honors listed in the proviso. The conditions barred the child from virtually every field of activity usually available to a gentleman. He could not enter the Navy, the Army or the Church, three careers normally open to sons of the nobility. The Church is not specifically mentioned in the proviso but appointments in the Church were under the authority of His Majesty. Indeed George III took a personal interest in the naming of Bishops and lesser dignitaries of the clergy.

James Louis was to be debarred from politics. He could not enter Parliament nor hold a job under the civil service. He would not be allowed to receive any grants of property at the disposal of the Crown.

It might seem peculiar to spell out the fact that a ten-year-old boy could never become a member of the Privy Council. However, that was an astute proviso, if anyone wished to block all possibility of James reaching a position of power in the Kingdom.

The Privy Council was a body of advisors to His Majesty roughly comparable to a modern Cabinet. The Council except for certain judicial duties had no executive or legislative power, but wielded influence. Some members of the Privy Council were there *ex officio,* but a private citizen, especially one of great wealth, could become a member of the Council if appointed by the King. James was due to inherit considerable wealth from his mother and if he had business acumen he might build it into a fortune. In such a case conceivably he might become chosen for the Privy Council, except for this proviso.

Some influence close to the Crown evidently had dictated these limitations and suspicion falls on the Duke of Northumberland. He is the only known person who would have any reason to fear the rise of James to prominence.

The very form of the petition is evidence that the Crown was aware of the parentage of James. Nowhere in the petition is there any mention of a surname for the applicant. He doubtless was known to be an illegitimate son of Northumberland, who had great influence at court. The Duchess was an intimate of Queen Charlotte and a godmother of one of the royal children. Northumberland had the advantage of not being active in politics, whereas most of the nobles were a trial to the King either in opposition or, if on the Tory side, difficult to control. George III felt at ease with Northumberland and could sympathize with his desire to forestall the possibility of a rival.

Opposition to the success of a son, which seems unnatural in modern social life, was customary in the Hanoverian tradition. Each of the King Georges hated the current Crown Prince. The Opposition party in Parliament customarily rallied around the oldest son, knowing that ultimately the King would die and they then would be in favor with the succession.

Obviously the former Sir Hugh Smithson (now Northumberland) was not in a parallel situation to royalty, but if his illegiti-mate son should come into prominence, rivaling his legitimate son, the fact could be embarrassing. It could cast a shadow over Northumberland's own eminence and be unpleasant for his legit-imate heir. The latter who had already grown to manhood did not give any evidence of inheriting his father's vigor. Hence, it was important for the Northumberland line to block any rise by James.

The barriers set up by the proviso were not publicized or gen-erally known, but they must have been very present in James' mind when he grew to maturity. As will appear, he became a scientist of considerable note. Most of his contemporaries of simi-lar ability were knighted—Sir Joseph Banks, Sir Davies Gilbert, Sir Charles Blagden, Sir Humphry* Davy—but not James. The pro-viso prevented such an honor being conferred upon him.

In later years, when James Smithson left his fortune to establish an institution in America, surprise was expressed in some quarters that he did not leave the money for such a project in Great Brit-ain. But the motivation was obvious. James Smithson's Govern-ment had rejected him.

* The name is spelled either Humphrey or Humphry in local contemporary sources.

Note: The naturalizing act for Jacques, otherwise James Louis, is cited in *Journals of the House of Lords* Vol. XXXIII, p. 686.

CHAPTER 4

Bright College Days

On the seventh of May, 1782, James Macie matriculated at Pembroke College, Oxford. The original biographer Rhees assumed that the college bills were paid by the father since Rhees said "nothing has been learned" of the mother's history. The college records indicate that James himself paid the charges and there is no evidence there as to what was the source of his income.

However, when in later years James was a prisoner of war in Germany, he wrote to Sir Joseph Banks in England mentioning that he could be addressed care of Messrs. Hoare, Bankers, Fleet Street. Fortunately this firm is still in business and its ancient archives have the records of the receipts and disbursements of Mrs. Elizabeth Macie and James.

Mrs. Macie opened her account in 1780. Her major deposit was eleven thousand pounds in bonds and there were more than two thousand pounds of receipts from half-dozen other sources, possibly rents or interest.

Subsequently she received twenty-six hundred pounds from a Mr. Graham, who later became a business agent for James. There was no account in the name of James, individually, until February, 1785, his third college year; but it is reasonable to suppose that he received cash sums from his mother during the first part of

James Smithson as an Oxford student

his college course, for he was only twenty years of age when he established his personal account.

It is possible if not probable that Northumberland contributed to James' education through his mother or by other indirection. The Duke also had an account with Messrs. Hoare established in 1779. The coincidence is not necessarily significant since Messrs. Hoare were one of the leading banking houses of London. The deposits of Northumberland were all made to a D. Parker and in the first year these amounted to thirty-seven thousand pounds. The record does not show how Mr. Parker disposed of the funds but the size of the amount suggests that he may have been the manager for the sizable Northumberland properties, meeting the payrolls, taxes, and various upkeep costs.

Whatever the source of income, James was enrolled as a "Gentleman Commoner," a distinction which meant that he was paying his own way and not a scholarship student. In fact he was one of the more prosperous undergraduates as the enrollment at Pembroke came generally from students of modest circumstances.

On the college books where the members of the various classes were listed there was a line for the name of a student's father. In the case of Macie, the space was left blank. Apparently the college was aware of James' parentage, though this might not have been known by the student body as he went by the name of Macie and the circumstances of his birth are not referred to in various of the diaries or other comments of his classmates. A college mate who became famous as Sir Davies Gilbert wrote in his diary "what is very curious, his father's name is omitted and he is merely stated to be the son of an Esquire."

There were other aspects of the entrance data of Macie which were significant. He was required to register in the entry book of Oxford University where the newcomers in the various colleges were listed. His name appears in the Latin form as follows:

Jacobus Ludovicus Macie e Col. Pem. Arm. Fil.

The abbreviations refer to Pembroke College and *Armiger Filius* namely bearer of arms, or having a coat of arms.

James clearly could not use the Northumberland arms, nor those of John Macie who had died before James was born; but his mother was entitled to use the Hungerford crest and various other arms in her ancestry. Apparently the University accepted James' right to claim the distinction from the maternal source. The chief practical usefulness for James was the right to use the designation "Esquire" after his name; and as an illegitimate son this might have some importance for him.

Another aspect of this particular registration list, according to the Bodleian Library, is that the signers affirmed their belief in the Thirty-nine Articles of Faith of the Church of England.

Pembroke was to a large degree a poor man's college. Rich and titled scions went to Christ Church, Trinity or other elite places according to the traditions of their families.

Pembroke, because of its low costs, was a haven for talented boys in relatively humble circumstances, boys who had won county scholarships. Its ranks were fed, for example, by the brightest graduates of Charterhouse School for which Pembroke provided an annual scholarship.

Pembroke's most famous graduate at the time of James' matriculation in 1782 had been Samuel Johnson. Johnson was so poor that he could not afford to go home during vacation periods. He was entitled to have his board the year around and so he stayed and was fed. Blackstone also was a notable alumnus.

This was a place where the boy of limited means without advantages of title could shine if he had the brainpower. Pembroke had then, and has through the ages, a substantial share of men of distinction who as undergraduates had come from modest homes.

James entered with the advantage of a somewhat bigger purse than most of his fellows. Week after week his payments for board were slightly higher than those of his classmates. The record exists. When the tabulation shows his expense at perhaps one pound, ten shillings per week most of his colleagues might be paying fifteen shillings.

Pembroke College had a typical liberal arts curriculum which included a thorough grounding in the Scriptures. The scholars attended daily chapel and James was consistently devout. In later years when fundamentalists attacked the new science as hostile to the supposedly complete truth as contained in the Bible, James was able to enter the lists effectively and good-humoredly, for he was fully familiar with the Inspired Word. In fact he held that to study the phenomena of the material world was to learn more about the wonders of the firmament. His classic defense of the validity of the scientific method was a forerunner of the eventual support of Darwinism, an issue which was fought throughout the Anglo-Saxon world a generation later and for fifty years after that.

St. Aldate's Church, which is still one of the major church edifices at Oxford, was and is the parish church for Pembroke. During Smithson's time the trustees were "high church," but the "low church" movement was simmering and in fact became

St. Aldate's Church, the parish church for Pembroke

Pembroke College, Oxford

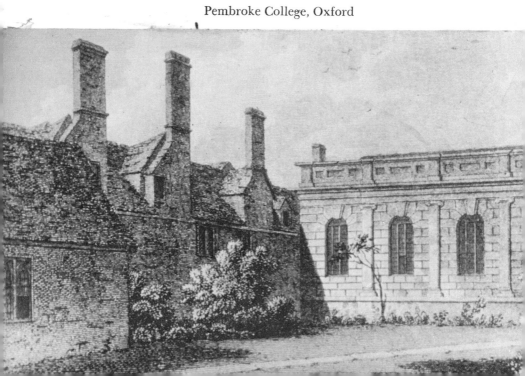

dominant in the parish not long after Smithson's demise. In general it was the "low church" clergy who were hospitable to science. (The report of the Jamesian defense appears in a subsequent chapter.)

Throughout his life Macie adhered to Christian belief, finding it consistent with modern science. In fact his scientific studies provided a bond with various of his many Catholic friends on the Continent. These included several priests in Italy and France who were foremost scholars in chemistry and mineralogy. Even in his last days at Genoa, Macie, who for some years had been known as James Smithson, was affiliated with the little English Chapel there, and he was buried in the Protestant cemetery on the heights of San Benigno.

The interest of the young undergraduate in natural·science was self-generated and extracurricular. There was no laboratory. Sir Davies Gilbert, when later he was President of the Royal Society, referred to James as the greatest chemical authority in the college. That branch of science was in a primitive state. James said of it shortly after his college days, "Chemistry is yet so new a science, what we know of it bears so small a proportion to what we are ignorant of; our knowledge in every department of it is so incomplete, consisting so entirely of isolated points, thinly scattered, like lurid specks on a vast field of darkness, that no researches can be undertaken without producing some facts leading to consequences which extend beyond the boundaries of their immediate object."

It is difficult to understand why a scientific approach, with a few exceptions, had been neglected for centuries, yet that was so. Now, as indicated earlier, zeal for the study of science and its applications was bursting out all over in France, Italy, Sweden, Germany, and England. James was fortunate in finding college mates who shared his enthusiasm. These included Gilbert, quoted above, whose name then was Giddy; William Higgins, a contumaceous rebel, who nevertheless was elected to the Royal Society; and Beddoes, who became an eminent physician.

An extracurricular activity always has a special appeal to under-graduates. In this case chemistry and the other physical sciences had their flavor of wickedness in the eyes of many of their elders. Why should undergraduates go about probing for the structure of the universe? The curiosity of these young men knew no bounds. In fact the young scientists did not limit themselves to any single phase. Smithson himself explored the mysteries of mineralogy, geology, biology, organic chemistry, electricity, and even cookery.

Macie's ambition was boundless. If Northumberland was in fact the man who closed the doors of worldly opportunity to James, the latter had a self-protective instinct. The field of science was new and no one had thought to forbid Macie from practicing it. He realized that as an undergraduate he would have difficulty in get-ting very far by his own unaided efforts; but he had the bright idea of attaching himself to men of prominence in whatever humble capacity might be available. On this principle he became a laboratory laborer for Henry Cavendish—a lowly job which proved to be probably the most important step in his entire career.

Cavendish was thirty-four years older than Macie; but he was one of the few men of the older generation who was interested in scientific investigation.

Cavendish was a brother of the third Duke of Devonshire and a brother-in-law of the Duke of Kent. His father had made meteoro-logical observations and had studied the behavior of mercury in barometric tubes. Thus Henry Cavendish's interest in scientific investigation had been instilled early.

In 1760 he had become a member of the Royal Society, which represented his only social interest, even though his wealth was enormous, amounting to over seven hundred thousand pounds. He had his laboratory in his large house on Bedford Square, and in it he became virtually a hermit, except for regular attendance at Royal Society gatherings and his entertaining of a few scientific acquaintances in his library once a week. Usually he ordered his solitary dinner by a daily note placed on the hall table and his female domestics had orders to keep out of his sight on pain of dismissal.

James Macie soon became a favorite of this odd character who employed the young man in various investigations. Hence it was that in his junior year Macie was able to attach himself to an expedition which included notable international scientists.

CHAPTER 5

Pioneer Adventure

Three men were due to have a continuing influence on the life of Macie. Cavendish of course was the first.

Sir Joseph Banks was perhaps the longest continuing influence, for Banks lived as long as Macie, though he was more than twenty years older. He was a man of extraordinary influence and vast accomplishment. He was President of the Royal Society for forty years and the range of his friendships may be seen by the size of his correspondence.

There is a catalog of several hundred printed pages listing the Banks correspondence in the South Kensington Museum, London. There are ten thousand items in the Sutro Library at San Francisco; also there are collections at Yale, Dartmouth, and New Zealand.

One of Banks' pursuits was that of horticulturalist and persons sent him samples of rare plants from all over the world. He was an explorer who visited the South Seas. His home in Soho Square, London, was a continuous meeting place for men of scientific interests.

Banks was in charge of the gardens at Kew Park. He studied the economics of the wool industry and improved the strain of merino sheep on the royal estates. He cultivated the good side of George III, who was ardently interested in applied science. As a result

Sir Joseph Banks
(Courtesy of the Royal Society)

Banks was appointed to the Privy Council, a post to which James was forbidden to aspire.

The third influence was Sir Charles Blagden, not yet knighted, who in Macie's younger days was secretary to Cavendish and cordial to Macie. Later he became an army doctor and was stationed for several years in America from where he wrote frequent reports to Banks on the flora and fauna of that area. Clearly the close association with these men was an education in itself and it is partly because of their interest that we are informed of James' initial adventure:

Under the university system, there were no classes during lengthy vacation periods, when the student was free to comport himself as he chose in reading or other preparation. He was not required to stay on campus and in fact few did. Macie saw in the situation an opportunity for field work. In fact in the new approach to science, field work was a chief source of enlightenment—aside from the scientific journals—for there were virtually no up-to-date books extant.

Macie learned in 1784 that there was to be an exploration to Fingal's Cave off the northwest coast of Scotland. The Cave was the start of a geologic rift which ran under the ocean all the way to Ireland.

The party was composed of a man named Thornton, who wrote travel pieces; Faujas de St. Fond, a French geologist; and Count Andrioni, an Italian. How the young undergraduate managed to attach himself to such a distinguished group is not known. But a journal which he kept of the event shows that he was included as a sort of water boy, generally in charge of chores.

The party set out from England in September 1784 and went through New Castle, Edinburgh, Glasgow, Dumbarton, Tarbet, Inverary, Oban, Arran, and the island of Staffa. They reached the first part of their destination, the seacoast village of Mull, on September 24, 1784. The second point was to be the island of Staffa, near the entrance to Fingal's Cave.

Macie left the party at this point to do some independent exploring in a rowboat. He found that the sea was so rough and the wind was so high that it was impossible to visit the Cave. Hence he returned to the mainland and set out for Staffa where he landed with some difficulty. On arrival he found that the main party had gone ahead and were already located in a house which appeared to be the only habitation on the island. His journal notes that they were "all crammed into one bad hut, though nine of ourselves beside the family; supped upon eggs, potatoes, and milk; lay upon hay, in a kind of barn.

"25th. Got up early, sea ran very high, wind extremely strong—no boat could put off. Breakfasted on boiled potatoes and milk; dined upon the same; only got a few very bad fish; supped on potatoes and milk; lay in the barn, firmly expecting to stay there for a week, without even bread."

Early in the morning of the 26th the man of the island wakened the party saying that the wind had dropped and therefore the time was opportune to get back to the mainland. James set off in a makeshift boat which used a plaid kilt for a sail and garters for ropes. The boat leaked so that it was necessary to bail constantly, but he made the landing successfully.

The party then made a stop at Oban, taking rooms for three days. James put in the time collecting fossils in a barrel and arranging for them to be sent by water to Edinburgh. When he came to depart the landlord charged him extra because of the fossils which had cluttered the room saying that Macie had brought "stones and dirt" into it.

Blagden, who had received reports of this adventure from Macie, had more details to offer than appeared in the journal. On the 17th of October he wrote a letter to Sir Joseph Banks on the subject. It seems that St. Fond had not crossed the water to Staffa after all. "His heart failed him when he came to the ocean and . . . he remained languishing on the mainland until their return." He says that all the others including Macie completed the journey, that Thornton was making drawings for the record and hence that Macie would be returning with a fuller account.

Oddly enough, though the trip had been an adventurous experience for Macie, it seems to have been a disappointment for the others. There is no mention of it to be found in the memoirs or letters of the other participants and no drawings by Thornton, even though he was in the habit of recording his trips in considerable detail.

Possibly their expedition was overshadowed even in their own minds by a sensational balloon ascension occurring about that time, which inflamed the popular interest and was in fact surveyed by Cavendish and Blagden, who checked the event with instruments.

Henry Cavendish had discovered hydrogen, had measured it as lighter than air, and had led the way to its being separated from the atmosphere for practical uses—notably as a filler-gas for balloons. Hitherto, the use of hot air as an inflatant for balloons had been impractical for obvious reasons, such as the difficulty of carrying aloft a stove to keep the air heated. Hydrogen, however, opened up new potentials for developing lighter-than-air vehicles which could scan the heavens. In the 1780's, within the space of a few years, some dozen newly designed balloons were built, mostly by French inventors and by some in Italy.

The British took little interest, though Cavendish personally studied the developments. The Germans were not alert.

However, in France balloon mania reached a high pitch. The balloon captured the imagination of the public. Crowds of thousands appeared on the scene whenever an ascension was scheduled. The government saw great possibilities in the new control of the air. For any promoter-inventor who could take the lead in this new field the potential rewards were fabulous. In France there were several leading contenders—the Montgolfier brothers; also Messieurs Charles, Robert, and Blanchard. Though the last three had English-sounding last names, they were as French as frogs' legs. Blanchard was the most belligerent. He knocked an intruder out of the basket of his balloon with a blow of the fist. On the other hand, a rival charged into the anchorage of the Blanchard balloon, broke the halyards, and thus delayed a scheduled flight by days. The truth about what Blanchard achieved in flight is hard to come by, for various of his hostile colleagues accuse him of "romancing."

It is a fact, however, that he built a balloon which made a flight from Chelsea on October 16, 1784. A professor of anatomy, Charles Sheldon, was a passenger, probably the first Englishman to undertake a cross-country balloon flight.

Cavendish and Blagden checked the course of the airship from a housetop on Putney Heath, and wrote a report on the event to Sir Joseph Banks.

James Macie, who was engaged on his Scotland adventure, was the potential scribe for this event; but it proved not to be a moment in history, despite great expectations. In theory, balloons were to become the eyes of the army, yet no government exploited the possibility—not Britain, and not France or Italy, who had pioneered this new potential.

CHAPTER 6

Prospects after College

Like many of the undergraduates at Pembroke, Davies Giddy had come from modest circumstances. His father was a clergyman. Not long after Davies' graduation he married a wealthy woman and, as frequently happened, he took her surname and ultimately became known as Sir Davies Gilbert.

In his college days at Pembroke he had become a great admirer and a close friend of James Macie. In fact he testified in future years to the outstanding ability of Macie. It was he who declared that Macie was the greatest chemical genius in the college.

Now on the 26th of May, 1786, Macie had just received the degree of Master of Arts.

The ceremonies had been concluded. Gilbert describes the scene in his diary: "On this day Mr. James Louis Macie . . . was created Master of Arts in the Convocation House. I remember his being rested on the upper end of the Bench on the Floor . . . that we walked back together when Macie exchanged his Cap for a Hat and then walked with me round Christ Church Meadow."

Macie never forgot this attention of Gilbert, and the friendship endured throughout Macie's life.

What future was there for Macie? Doubtless he could always have a job with Cavendish and he could not then foresee the unusual help that Cavendish was soon to give him. Macie was

Sir Davies Gilbert
(Courtesy of the Royal Society)

barred from all the normal careers (by the provisos of his naturalization papers); yet there should be some way of pursuing his passion for natural science,—probably not in a faculty post where the chief appointments might be at the pleasure of the Crown—but somehow independently.

One shudders to think what might have been Macie's destiny if he had not fallen into independent wealth provided by his mother. Within a short time after graduation he received two minor fortunes, one a gift of twenty-five hundred pounds and another of six thousand. These windfalls, of course, would be adequate for anyone content to lead a life of leisure, but by themselves they would not assure a career for a man of science. Some prestige, some platform would be needed to give authentic credit to his discoveries.

But in a few months after taking his degree he was told by Mr. Cavendish that the latter was going to propose him for membership in the Royal Society and that he would become the youngest man ever to receive nomination to that august body.

The wording of the proposal and the names of the proposers were a high tribute to the young man:

James Lewis Macie, Esq., M.A., late of Pembroke College, Oxford, Street, Golden Square—a gentleman well versed in various branches on Natural Philosophy, and particularly in Chymistry and Mineralogy, being desirous of becoming a Fellow of the Royal Society, we whose names art hereto subscribed do, from our personal knowledge of his merit, judge him highly worthy of that honour and likely to become a very useful and valuable Member. signed Richard Kirwan. C. F. Greville. C. Blagden. H. Cavendish. David Pitcairn.

Macie was admitted as a Fellow of the Society on the 26th of April, 1787. Cavendish was an intimate of Sir Joseph Banks, President of the Society. Thus James met Banks under most favorable auspices; and Banks became his friend and mentor.

Judged by its own standards the Royal Society was the most exclusive group in England, an aristocracy of brains. For James Macie it was his social club in which he ranked with the best. Also, it was an active club with weekly meetings, discussions, exchange of views with other members on the latest discoveries on the structure of material matter. The news that poured into those weekly meetings was not equalled in excitement until the astrophysical breakthroughs of the 1960's.

Macie was unselfishly devoted to the Society and to building up a young membership. Considering the background of his life, he understandably could have rested on the prestige of having been the youngest member ever elected.

But no. Macie first sponsored the man most likely to outshine him, at least in Society affairs. Giddy, later Sir Davies Gilbert, tells the story in his diary:

"June 5, 1789. I called on Mr. Macie, received very civilly." Macie was in London.

"June 11, 1789. Macie introduced me to Sir Joseph Banks of the Royal Society."

No greater favor could have been conferred. Macie laid his full influence at the disposal of his friend. Gilbert was not blind to the fact, for his diary next notes:

"June 16, 1789. I called on Macie in the evening."

What did the two discuss? Naturally there is no record; but soon Gilbert also was a Fellow of the Royal Society. He rose in the ranks of the Society until he became President, succeeding Banks.

Macie doubtless approved of Gilbert's rise all along the line, for Macie repeatedly welcomed new young members—both Pembroke graduates and others.

The Royal Society of London was the most noted scientific body in Great Britain. It was organized in 1660 to encourage scientific discovery and invention and to promote industrial progress. Scientists were elected to membership only on the recommendation of several members, and usually only fifteen candidates were voted upon annually. The meetings in the early days were held at the Bull Head Tavern in Cheapside and later in Gresham College.* Initially the number of members was limited to fifty-five, and to persons of the degree of baron, fellows of the College of Physicians and certain professors of "mathematics, physic and natural science." One of its most distinguished members was Isaac Newton, elected in 1671 and named President in 1703, a post which he held for twenty-four years.

Sir Joseph Banks had been elected, President in 1780, an office which he held for forty years. James Macie was an ardent member of the Society all his life and an occasional contributor to the Society's magazine *Philosophical Transactions* which was accepted internationally as one of the most authoritative publications in the scientific world. (In 1801 James was granted the privilege by the Crown to change his name to James Smithson. Hence his scientific papers will be found under the name of Macie or Smithson, depending upon the date when they appeared.)

In view of Smithson's consistent loyalty to the Society it is curious that there has been an oft-reported canard to the effect that he became disaffected with it toward the end of his life.

The basis for the story originated in a comment attributed to Louis Agassiz in a debate in the United States House of Repre-

* Then a notable institution, independent of the universities, administered by the mayor and aldermen of London, intended for education of the middle classes. It lasted until 1710.

sentatives on February 27, 1855. In a letter to a professor at Harvard, Agassiz is quoted as saying, "I ought not to omit mentioning a circumstance to which the United States owes the legacy of Smithson, which I happen accidentally to know, and which is much to the point concerning the management of the Smithsonian Institution. Smithson had already made his will and had left his fortune to the Royal Society of London, when certain scientific papers were offered to that learned body for publication. Notwithstanding his efforts to have them published in their *Transactions,* they were refused, upon which he changed his will, and made his bequest to the United States. It would be easy to collect in London more minute information upon this occurrence and should it appear desirable, I think I can put a committee in the way of learning all the circumstances."

Agassiz had come to America from Switzerland in 1846 and had a distinguished reputation. The fact that this letter was offered on the floor of Congress impressed many persons, even though Agassiz as authority for his statement merely said "which I happen accidentally to know."

The story was circulated from time to time in various forms. The seeming mystery as to why Smithson should leave his money to the United States rather than to his own country is cleared up when one knows the circumstances of his personal life. Also he was well acquainted with various scientists who were American born or who had traveled in America.

Agassiz has long since passed away, and only recently was his suggestion that the rumor could be checked in London acted upon. In 1963 inquiry at the office of the Royal Society brought the reply that not in the minutes or in any other records of the Society is there or has there been any evidence of disaffection by Smithson or a changed will.

James, even though a new member, was soon given the opportunity to prepare a paper on a subject which at that time commanded considerable interest, namely, the essence of tabasheer. This was a substance found in the joints of bamboo. It was widely used in the Orient to cure eye infections and had been adopted to some extent in the western world as a home remedy, though not officially accepted by the medical profession. As there were various types of bamboo in different sections of the Orient having variations in the tabasheer, extended laboratory tests were necessary. In this connection, Macie was complimented by having among his laboratory assistants no lesser authorities than Cavendish and Banks!

The experiment had wider significance than might appear on the surface, for it served to illustrate Macie's belief that all matter is interrelated. The atomic theory had been developed by certain of his colleagues at Pembroke, but Macie's habit was to apply minute testing of any hypothesis and not to accept it unless it had been established by concrete evidence. Tabasheer was usually found as a liquid secretion; yet sometimes it occurred as a solid within the joint, about the size of a "BB" shot.

Dr. Russell, a member of the Society, at a prior meeting had introduced seven parcels of tabasheer which he had acquired from various sources. Some came from Hydrabad and some from Masulapatam. The learned Doctor had not subjected his specimens to laboratory analysis (see *Philosophical Transactions,* Vol. LXXX, p. 283); hence the opportunity for further research was embraced by Macie. The various tests which he undertook were described in his paper running to several thousand words. To present the full report would require a disproportionate amount of space here, but a few sample paragraphs will illustrate the method. Of one sample Macie stated:

"(B) This tabasheer could not be broken by pressure between the fingers; but by the teeth it was easily reduced to powder. On first chewing it felt gritty, but was soon ground to impalpable particles.

"(C) Applied to the tongue, it adhered to it by capillary attraction.

"(D) It had a disagreeable earthy taste, something like that of magnesia.

"(E) No light was produced either by cutting it with a knife, or by rubbing two pieces of it together, in the dark; but a bit of this substance, being laid on a hot iron, soon appeared surrounded with a feeble luminous *aureole*. By being made red hot, it was deprived of this property of shining when gently heated; but recovered it again, on being kept for two months.

"(F) Examined with the microscope, it did not appear different from what it does to the naked eye.

"(G) A quantity of this tabasheer which weighed 75.5 gr. in air, weighed only 41.1 gr. in distilled water whose temperature was 52.5 F. which makes its specific gravity to be very nearly $= 2.188$.

"Mr. Cavendish, having tried this same parcel when become again quite dry, found its specific gravity to be $= 2.169$."

Macie tested various samples by burning them in a red hot crucible, by soaking them in water for five hours, by treating them with nitric acid, vitriolic acid and a solution of crystals of soda. The material assumed quite different forms, changing into jellies, a kind of glass, a powder. The samples changed color under specific treatments. Sometimes the material was effervescent and sometimes inert.

In addition to these experiments, Macie reported, "A singular circumstance has presented itself. A green bamboo, cut in the hothouse of Dr. Pitcairn at Islington, was judged to contain tabasheer in one of its joints, from a rattling noise discoverable on shaking it; but being split by Sir Joseph Banks, it was found to contain, not ordinary tabasheer, but a solid pebble, about the size of half a pea.

"Externally this pebble was of an irregular rounded form, of a dark-brown or black color. Internally it was reddish brown, of a close dull texture, much like some martial siliceous stones. In one corner there were shining particles, which appeared to be crystals, but too minute to be distinguished even with the microscope."

When this paper was published in the *Philosophical Transactions* for the year 1791, part II, page 368, it created a sensation. *The Monthly Review* for January 1792 reported on the significance of the experiments. "We have seen in a former paper that tabasheer is a vegetable production, formed by spontaneous concretion from a fluid in the cavities of the bamboo cane. Its chemical constitution, however, is very different from what might be expected in a body of such an origin. The experiments of Mr. Macie, very judiciously executed, and here stated in detail, show it to be a siliceous earth, nearly the same thing with common flint that has been attenuated by artificial solution."

As the magazine comment suggested, the similarity of the vegetable product from bamboo with the characteristics of common flint were a demonstration of the interrelationship of the structure of the physical world. Macie's reputation was made. As much as four years later an Englishman consular officer stationed in Genoa, writing to Sir Joseph Banks, gave Macie as a reference for an Italian priest who was also a scientist saying that the Reverend Father "is well known to the chemical [sic]. Mr. Macie who analysed the tabaschir. . . . "

CHAPTER 7

Early London Days

Ever since James had been naturalized as a British subject he had prudently resided in England. Had he returned to Paris before reaching his majority he might have had some difficulty in preserving his naturalized status.

He had remained under the care of his guardian, having an address in St. Mary leBow parish. From circumstantial evidence, it seems probable that he attended Charterhouse School in London for several years (though the school cannot confirm this, as the records were not kept for day scholars).

By the time James was six years old, he had a baby brother, born in August 1771. The boy went by the name of Henry Louis Dickinson. His father, however, was the same as James' father, namely the Duke of Northumberland. The Dickinson subterfuge was so well maintained that the boy ultimately had a successful army career under that name. There seems to be no doubt as to the true parentage. The boy was listed in a school record as "a natural son of Northumberland"; and Rhees, writing years later, stated that the Duke had, besides James, "another natural son, who was known as Henry Louis Dickinson." Rhees habitually did not cite his sources, but he hardly would have made such an assertion without some basis. He evidently did not know who was the mother.

The Duke had three legitimate children, two boys and a girl, within the first ten years of his marriage. The Duchess was living and aged forty-nine when he had the first affair with Elizabeth Macie, in 1764.

The Duchess lived until 1776, but His Grace apparently went on the rampage in his latter years as he approached sixty. Not only did he have this second son by Elizabeth, but during the 1770's he had two illegitimate daughters. The elder was named Philadelphia Percy and the younger, Dorothy Percy.

There seems to be no record of the mother in that case, though the girls were sisters and devoted to each other.*

Apparently, they were wellborn, for the Duke, in due course, took them into his household and treated them as his own daughters. Each died in the early 90's, and each was buried in Westminister Abbey in the South Cross, according to the Abbey *Register.*

By what process Elizabeth hit upon the name Henry Louis Dickinson is a mystery. Her will implies that it was not a true name, for it mentions "my son Henry Louis Dickinson, and who was lately entered by that name at Charterhouse School, London." (The spelling of Dickinson or Dickenson was used interchangeably.)

If, in fact, Elizabeth had been married to a man named Mark Dickenson prior to her marriage to Macie (as mentioned earlier) some twenty years before the birth of her second son, that might have been her inspiration to use the Dickinson name. The Hungerford pedigree, as drawn up by the Reverend Mr. Brown, lists the earlier marriage and states that it was "dissolved." Also, written in by hand is the name of Henry as the son of Mark. That seems highly improbable and also, of course, is contravened by the evidence of the Duke as the true father. In the various family wills, there is no mention of any other Dickinson prior to Henry Louis.

* The mother, in a letter by a contemporary, is asserted to be a Mrs. Margaret Marriott. Dorothy's will left all her possessions to a Mrs. Marriott, though without explanation.

Also there may be a hidden drama in the parish books of St. George's, Hanover Square, which lists the marriage in 1774 of an Elizabeth Macie to a William Channell. The coincidence of the woman's name is provocative, especially as James' mother at the time was living in St. George's parish. It was usual and presumably profitable in that era for a man to volunteer as a husband to lend respectability to an embarrassing situation and to disappear forever after the ceremony. Such an event took place in the same parish in the case of the famous Quaker, Hannah Lightfoot, who had been allegedly admired by Prince George, the future George III, before he came to the Throne. Her emergency husband vanished after the wedding ceremony and was not heard from again.

The complexity of Elizabeth Macie's life had a bearing on the duties thrust upon her older son. In her will, made in 1789, she left everything to James, with the proviso that he reserve two thousand pounds in cash, plus certain other income, to provide for the education of his brother Henry and set him up in one of the professions. If James should die first the entire estate would be left to Henry; otherwise James would get it all. The properties were substantial, including a town house in Upper Charlotte Street, Fitzroy Square, plus several country places, chattels, and an unspecified amount of cash and securities.

Mrs. Macie died in 1800; Henry had been boarded with the Headmaster of Charterhouse in 1780 and had remained at the school until 1784. At the time of his mother's death and apparently since he had finished school, he had been employed in the offices of the Graham firm. In March 1790, he purchased a commission as ensign in the British Army. From then on James was free of responsibility for his brother.

James in 1790 was twenty-five years of age and unmarried; and he never married. His position was cruelly unfortunate. He had prestige in the world of science and he had money, but his illegitimate birth was a stigma which could haunt him and any family he might sire. It will be recalled that the provisio in his naturalization papers barred him from any public career of honor.

Illegitimate birth was not necessarily a social handicap to a girl in the upper classes if her father chose to provide her with a substantial dowry, but with a man, the problem was different; he had no name to offer, no clan relationship. Family connections were highly important in the society of the day. Most of the great families were interrelated and, barring occasional feuds, the individual members helped one another.

The Duke had died in 1786, which was a blessing as far as James was concerned, for the old man had never shown any disposition to provide any form of preferment for James. In fact, any substantial favor would go naturally to one of his legitimate children. The oldest son, of course, inherited the dukedom, while the second son was created Lord Beverley and received the estate of Alnwick. The legitimate daughter died unmarried.

James devoted his full energies to the career which was open to him, namely, scientific discovery. Until the death of Cavendish in 1810, Macie had the use of the laboratories in Bedford Square. Indeed Henry Cavendish welcomed all the young scientists to regard his house as their sanctuary. Soon after Cavendish died, James and various associates had the facilities of elaborate laboratories at 21 Albemarle Street for the use of qualified scientists, under the auspices of the newly formed Royal Institution. It was at this address, for example, where Davy, inventor of the miner's lamp, worked. Indeed, Britain's bright flame was kept glowing in those years, 1780–1820, when a few devoted men carried the torch.

Meanwhile, James adopted geology and mineralogy as his particular subjects. This involved much of his time in field work, wherein he made exhaustive studies of rock conditions in various parts of England. It was while exploring in Derbyshire and Somersetshire that he discovered a new type of zinc ore, which unexpectedly brought him a form of immortality by including his name forever in the dictionary. He had analyzed this ore as distinctive from any other previously identified. The significance of this discovery will be discussed in a later chapter on "The Name of Smithsonite."

The mature James Smithson

Macie was due to spend the decade of the 1790's in research in many countries, and not until the end of that decade did he begin to think of applying for legal permission to change his name to Smithson.

Curiously, he undertook the petition because his mother, "during her lifetime," had expressed the wish that he adopt the Smithson name. As the Duke had died in 1786, there could be no objection from him. Macie, in his petition, made no mention of his paternity, but said, "Elizabeth Macie, late of the city of Bath and of Durnford, otherwise Hungerford Durnford in the county of Wilts, widow deceased, having during her lifetime expressed an earnest desire that the petitioner and his issue [there was none] 'should take and use the surname of Smithson instead of that of Macie,' the petitioner is desirous of complying therewith."

The request of Elizabeth is evidence of her concern for the

welfare of her older son, and suggests that her attachment to the Duke may have been the chief romance in her life. In any case, James' fame should have a better tag than the name Macie. There were few Macies extant by 1800, and to use that name could raise questions. Smithson was a large clan containing various talented persons. The connection with the Duke would not immediately arise, for he had changed his name by Act of Parliament to Percy, and he conferred that name on his bastard daughters.

On February 16, 1801, the Prime Minister in the King's name granted the petition of James to be named Smithson, affirming that the "declaration be recorded in our College of Arms to the end that our Officers of Arms and all others upon occasion may take full notice and have knowledge thereof."

Note: The will of Elizabeth Macie and the granting of the petition for James to adopt the name of Smithson may be consulted at the Public Record Office.

The vital statistics of the Northumberland family are to be found in the Westminster Abbey *Register*.

Persons visiting Westminster Abbey may find the Northumberland tomb in the St. Nicholas Chapel on the right-hand side as one enters. The tomb is a rectangular stone sarcophagus with no coffin visible. Against the back wall, above the sarcophagus, is a polished black stone slab in tribute to the Duchess and the three legitimate children.

Reference is frequently made to the text of the coffin plate, with the inference that this description of the Duke was a public tribute. However, the plate is not visible and the extravagant tone of the language suggests that it was prepared by the family. The text begins "the most high puissant & most noble Prince Hugh Percy, Duke and Earl of Northumberland." Then follow his other titles and positions, including "Vice-Admiral of the county of Northumberland & of all America."

There is no desire to underrate this man who from humble beginnings made an extraordinary financial success and apparently had taste in art and architecture. He is reputed to have had an income of forty thousand pounds per annum or more. The habit of adulation of persons in high places is illustrated in the memoirs of the Frenchman L. Dutens when he describes the Duchess, tracing her descent from Charlemagne. He also gives her credit for the wealth of the family; but, as noted elsewhere, it seems that the business abilities of the Duke established the properties on a paying basis.

CHAPTER 8

Early Years in Europe

Throughout the decade of the 1790's Smithson's reputation grew in the Continental countries. Some of the European scientists were members of the Royal Society and in turn some of the English scientists were members of French and Italian academies. As mentioned before, the young scientists generally had a mutuality of interests and friendships which overcame national barriers.

Macie was especially attached to the French and Italian coteries by temperament as well as by admiration of their accomplishments. He was drawn also to the Continent by the differences in its mineral structure from that of England. In France and in Italy where there were meteorites, these varied from the size of marbles to units weighing several tons. To a geologist, this material was as provocative as moon-watching to later generations. Analyzing these particles might give a wider understanding of the structure of the universe beyond the earth. In fact, studying the composition of meteorites, the minerals and gases involved, is of new importance in our space age. Such analysis is a continuing activity at Smithsonian's Astrophysical Observatory at Cambridge, Massachusetts.

Another fascinating field was the study of lava from the volcanoes which dotted Southern Europe. This might tell something of the structure inside the earth. The various countries of Europe, moreover, had a wide diversity in their geologic formations and Macie traversed many areas in Western Europe collecting samples for his cabinets. That was a standard occupation for the geologists of the various countries. They exchanged specimens with one another with all the zeal of stamp collectors. As Smithson said at one point, life was too short for any one geologist to assemble a substantial cabinet in his own lifetime.

Among the countries which Smithson visited was Germany. Here he seemingly had no great sympathy with the people. An Italian lady whom he met in Rome wrote to a friend in Florence saying "Our friend, the philosopher Macie, is here. He passed through Germany and says that among 26 million men he found only one who had common sense; that fellow was an obscure apothecary and he was touched in the head, *testa curiosa*." Presumably Macie was jesting even though he felt an undercurrent of truth in the remark. Conceivably also the efficient German spy system could have discovered this letter and forwarded its sentiments to headquarters, for later on Macie encountered serious trouble in Hamburg.

The German scientific group kept mostly within its own ranks. The chief man was Martin Klaproth, a scientist and mineralogist who had published several noteworthy papers which had come into the possession of Macie and others in the Royal Society. Klaproth was respected by his opposite numbers in other countries but he was not inclined to fraternize with *Ausländers*. He had a supreme confidence, shared by many of his countrymen, that Germany was the headquarters of scientific knowledge. Macie traveled in Germany and visited Hamburg, where Klaproth resided. If Klaproth showed Macie any hospitality, no record of this has been found, despite a diligent search of the local newspapers and journals of the time.

Macie's impression of the German people in that period was shared even by some of their enlightened leaders. Frederick Perthes, a German patriot, editor, and resident of Hamburg, had pride in his country's potential, but despaired over her sluggishness. He wrote to a friend, "Has not Germany for many years been the general Academy of Sciences for all Europe? All that was discovered or expounded, felt or thought in or out of Germany, was at once generalized by the Germans and elaborated into a form which might further the progress of humanity. In so far as we Germans had any vitality, we had it not for ourselves alone, but for Europe."

Probably French, Italian, and English scientists would not have agreed to this claim of German superiority, and Perthes himself was discouraged, saying, "We have every right to take credit to ourselves for intellectual wealth and for depth of character, but, alas! We have never known how to use our treasures. We have never given a general education, or a general aptitude to our people."

Perthes proposed to publish a journal which would champion a united Germany. His initial goal was to establish a national museum. In fact, he proposed to call the journal "The National Museum," and he sent copies of his prospectus to all parts of Germany. However, the temper and policies of the country thwarted his intentions. An alliance was forming between Austria, Russia, and Denmark.

In the early stages no one could be sure what policy this alliance would adopt. It might exclude England and also be opposed to France. The politics of Europe were continually shifting. Even some of the German states feuded with each other.

Perthes hoped that the alliance would result in aid to Germany. However, the German leaders were overwhelmed emotionally by the successes of Napoleon, and cast their lot on his side. Perthes said that the Government had clearly shown its "self-seeking imbecility by the character of their submission to Napoleon." The expectation of the Government that their submission to the conqueror would mean prosperity and partnership was in vain.

Immediately after the French occupation of Hamburg, all intercourse with England was prohibited on pain of death, all English property was declared forfeit, and all goods purchased from

English dealers, although paid for, were confiscated. Perthes saw that under those conditions, the hope of a united Germany must be forgotten. The idea of a National Museum was obviously an impossibility at this time. "Napoleon seeks only himself . . . he is a devil incarnate, because, like no other, he has made himself his god," Perthes wrote.

Prior to the rise of Napoleon, Macie had been an ardent admirer of France and the French scientists; and his loyalty to the latter never wavered. He was in France as late as the year 1789 when the French Revolution was in its early stages. Initially, he was sympathetic to the cause. He had been able to see the long-time corruption of the French court and was naturally favorable to an anti-royalty movement, feeling that he himself had suffered from the rigors of a traditional system in England. As an internationalist, his mind was open to new ideas. He was familiar with the American Revolution in general terms. Benjamin Franklin had been a member of the Royal Society. Franklin had founded the American Philosophical Society at Philadelphia, similar in purpose to the Royal Society. Unrest was in the air throughout the Western world. In 1792, Macie wrote from Paris (he was living in the Hôtel du Parc Royal, Rue de Colombier):

"*Ça ira* is growing to be the song of England, of Europe, as well as of France. Men of every rank are joining in the chorus. Stupidity and guilt have had a long reign, and it begins, indeed, to be time for justice and common sense to have their turn. . . . the office of king is not yet abolished, but they daily feel the inutility, or rather, great inconvenience, of continuing it and its duration will probably not be long. May other nations at the time of their reforms, be wise enough to cast off at first the contemptible incumbrance."

Curiously, some of the earlier biographical sketches have been apologetic over this declaration by Macie, suggesting that as he was young, perhaps that this should not be regarded as a statement of his final political philosophy. However the whole pattern of his life was consistent with that point of view. The fact that he ultimately left his fortune to America, in case he should have no living heirs, is an indication of his basic sympathies, even though he justifiably claimed royal and noble blood from his mother's side.

Macie was a republican rather than a democrat. He believed in the validity of good stock. His alluding to his relationship to the Duke of Northumberland which he emphasized in his will may have been no more than a desire to convince the courts that his will was entitled to important attention. Seemingly Macie had no close social contacts with the Northumberlands—not that he was necessarily scorned by them, but their eminence was achieved on a whole series of principles foreign to his own beliefs.

The Declaration of Independence, which had electrified most of the Western world outside of Britain and had stirred the Whig party in England, had hardly penetrated the consciousness of the Tory group.

Parenthetically it should be observed that the scientific community was in various of its members pro-Colonial. However, Sir Joseph Banks, as mentioned elsewhere, was close to George III in management of the royal properties and as an economist for the Kingdom, especially in the wool trade. Presumably Banks, who after all was not in politics, could not have influenced George III or warned him of the *dies irae*, for at this stage His Majesty was leaving·the management of colonial affairs to the Secretary of the Colonies, Lord George Germaine.

Science was fashionable in Florence due to sponsorship of the Duke of Tuscany. He gave financial support to scientific bureaus in the Government and made quarters available in the Pitti Palace.

Macie's particular friends included Ottavio Tozzetti, a botanist who was director of the "Natural Sciences" Department; Anton Vassalli-Eandi, inventor of an electrometer; and Giovanni Fabbroni, director of the department of "Physics and Natural History" (Tozzetti's work seemingly had to do chiefly with organic material and Giovanni's with inorganic).

Macie had not only the fascination of the pursuit of knowledge, but also a sense of fraternity in belonging to an elect group who knew more about the composition of the world than did the ordi-

nary citizen. When he was in Florence, he and Fabbroni exchanged items of information and also social amenities. Macie invited Fabbroni to dinner or breakfast day after day. Breakfast was
sometimes at 8:30, sometimes at 9:00, and often as late as 10:00
A.M. The dinner hour also was flexible. It might be at 3:30 P.M., or
possibly as late as 5:00. Fabbroni kept a record of these invitations,
and in one instance only did he decline, replying, "I promised to
go out with my wife this evening following the dinner hour, and
must therefore decline your honorable invitation."

Macie (his name was not yet Smithson) was able to hold up his
end socially as he currently was worth over six thousand pounds
and had his own establishment in Florence. An inventory of his
possessions at one time included a horse and carriage, a sixty-five-
piece set of table silver, sixteen shirts, thirteen pairs of stockings,
nineteen cravats, and so on. The scientist of that day needed to
have private means, as there usually was no money in scientific
research as such. Furthermore, while some scientists held profes-
sorial chairs Macie was barred from any official preferment in
England.

International travel and study required one to be fluent in several languages. Within the same Florentine visit, Macie addressed
Fabbroni in English, French, and Italian with equal facility, oft-
times using two languages in the same letter. It may be assumed
that he had some command of German, also, as he traveled frequently in that country.

When he was on the Continent Macie kept in touch with English periodicals, and on one occasion he reported to Fabbroni, "I
find, in an English newspaper, which I read this morning, that
about the middle of last month, there was a sale of some of Mr.
Page's cattle; one bull, called Shakespeare, sold for 400 guineas,
another, two years old, for 84 guineas, and one of 3 years sold for
70 guineas! You see whatever footing agriculture is upon at present in England, and you will not wonder that Kings have farms.
Indeed at this rate, it will soon only be Kings that will be able to
have them."

Again, Macie informed Fabbroni of a magazine item referring to a purported English discovery of how to make brick which would float on water. Macie commented that such a process was thought to have been known to the ancients.

Macie's enthusiasm for Italy was maintained over a period of some years, especially from 1793 to 1798 where he was in frequent correspondence with Fabbroni, Tozzetti, and others. Among the latter was a Roman priest, Father Petrini, who was a mineralogist. He exchanged geological specimens with Macie, who not only corresponded with him directly but also mentions him with respect when writing to others. Father Petrini was apparently responsible for Macie's spending a considerable amount of time in Rome, for initially Macie had not expected to find that city rewarding. In fact as he wrote to Fabbroni in 1793, "I have derived here no small pleasure and advantage from the acquaintance of Father Petrini who is a pleasing and informed man and really possessed of a cabinet collection of specimens more extensive and complete than I should have expected in a town which, though so celebrated a capitol, is so far removed from the mineral, the commercial, and I had almost said the scientific world."

There was a considerable affiliation of temperament between the advanced thinkers in Italy and the liberal element in England—using the word liberal in the general sense. The Whigs such as William Pitt the elder, Edmund Burke, and Henry Seymour Conway were closer to their counterparts in Europe than they were to the Court party, the so-called Tories in their own country. The woman who was quoted earlier writing to Fabbroni regarding Macie's comment on the Germans seemingly was aware of the English-speaking world judging by various references. She mentions the "Bahama-like sky of Italy" and sending some flannel, an English product, to Fabbroni. She added:

"I sent you five months ago an elegant and learned life of Lorenzo the Magnificent written by one Roscoe; but the courier took it by mistake to Sr. Hamilton in Naples who seems to have taken possession of it. Milord will write to you regarding it. You write to him too and help yourself to obtain the pleasure of reading a very fine thing.

"Indeed it is a shameful thing for the Florentines that an Englishman had to celebrate a person so worthy of a joyous reminiscence."

Then she mentions in closing "the last letter of Priestley." Priestley, who previously had been well acquainted with the Florentine group, was already in residence in America.

Priestley was the oldest of the group in terms of years but he had a lively and inquiring mind which made him feel at home with the Florentines. He had been raised in a strict nonconformist home and had become a Presbyterian minister. He had held several pastorates and also taught school. In his teaching years he pursued scientific studies, especially in chemistry and electricity. At one period he was a companion and a librarian to Lord Shelburne (who was in turn a friend of the Hungerford connection). This post gave him the opportunity to travel in Holland, Germany, France, and Italy. He became a passionate advocate of the French Revolution and of the newly-formed United States of America. His views made him highly unpopular in England. He changed from Calvinism to Unitarianism, and he harbored a chemistry laboratory in the parsonage. When he was a pastor in Birmingham, preaching unpopular doctrines, a mob burned down his chapel and his house. That was in 1791. It was during this period that he became well acquainted with the Florentine coterie and in 1794 he emigrated to America where he spent the last ten years of his life as an honored citizen.

Another America-Florentine tie was the friendship between Fabbroni and Thomas Jefferson. Jefferson's famous residence in Virginia was named Monticello, said to be in honor of a village (Monticello) near Florence which was associated with the reputation of Fabbroni and his discovery of a new type of ore, an alloy of lime, iron oxide, and silica. The ore was named Monticellite.

After his Italian journeys, Macie returned to England. From London, in September 1798, he wrote to Tozzetti, this time in

French and in reference chiefly to his assemblages in England of geological specimens which he offered to trade for European specimens. He also asked for the health of Father Petrini and introduced Tozzetti to Dr. Thompson, probably the future editor of a scientific magazine to which Macie became a frequent contributor.

A significant conclusion of the letter is Macie's request that in the future he be addressed as James Macie Esq., Upper Charlotte Street, Fitzroy Square, London. He had come a considerable distance along the path of prosperity—lodgings in John Street, Bentinck Street, Clarges Street in the West End near Green Park, and now Upper Charlotte Street, the town house ultimately left to him by his mother.

Within two years more he was to become a charter member of the Royal Institution which was supported initially by the elite of the brains, the wealth and the nobility of Great Britain.

CHAPTER 9

A Royal Institution for the People

In the years 1800 and 1801 there came into being a new body, called the Royal Institution, which was devoted particularly to making knowledge, especially the new discoveries in science, available to the general public. There were to be no social or educational barriers. *Ho! Everyone that thirsteth.* Its origin partook of the miraculous, for, in the new tone of the age, it was underwritten by those of the nation's elite who had the personal means to satisfy their own quests for knowledge and were glad to make the opportunity for others—*noblesse oblige.*

There were three hundred and thirty-one charter members, called proprietors. Of these, fifty-four were fellows of the Royal Society. Several were fellows of other groups—such as the Royal Asiatic Society founded in 1784, the Linnean Society (for promoting zoology and botany) established in 1788—devoted to special interests.

A list of the original members printed at the time is available in the Banks Collection at the Sutro Library, San Francisco. Here, in addition to the Royal Society fellows, one finds the Duke of Bedford, the Duke of Bridgewater, and the Duke of Somerset (who was a relative both of Mrs. Elizabeth Macie and the Duchesss of Northumberland). Josiah Wedgwood, the potter, was a member, also the suave Earl of Chesterfield, William Blake, the artist and poet, several members of Parliament, William Wilberforce, the abolitionist, Earl Stanhope; and from the FRS group, Cavendish, Banks, and James Smithson. (Smithson's name appears thus. Although the first official meeting of the Royal Institution was November 7, 1800, Smithson had won the right to use his new name before the list was printed.) The gathering of such an august group was well-nigh miraculous both because of the human effort involved and because the initial fee (and by no means the last) was sixty guineas* per person, all for an idea which was still to be translated into action.

The idea, namely, the stated purpose of the Royal Institution, was

For diffusing the knowledge and facilitating the general introduction of useful mechanical inventions and improvements and for teaching by courses of philosophical lectures and experiments the application of science to the common purposes of life.

As might be expected the chief man in enlisting the group was none other than Sir Joseph Banks. The attitude of mind of Sir Joseph Banks is revealed in a letter which he wrote dated January 26, 1802, to the French representative in England when Napoleon had restored France to a major world power.

He wrote, "the cooperation of those employed in enlarging the limits 'of human knowledge ought not to be interrupted by the enmity of their respective nations; the armistice of science should among wise people be perpetual."

In his modest way Banks had impressed his view by his sheer example on many of the enlightened minds of the age. He was without self-importance. Fanny Burney, the diarist, gives her impression of him from his visit to their Majesties at Windsor. She was at Windsor Castle on the Royal Household staff when Sir Joseph Banks happened to be at the customary afternoon tea. She said of him: "Sir Joseph was so exceedingly shy that we made no sort of acquaintance at all. If instead of going round the world he

* Est.: $360.00, in present purchasing power.

had only fallen from the moon, he could not appear less versed in the usual modes of a tea-drinking party."

But Miss Burney realized that her comment might be irrelevant. She was evidently aware of Sir Joseph's greatness, for she continued, "But what, you will say, has a tea-drinking party to do with a botanist, a man of science, a president of the Royal Society?"

It required someone with the prestige of Sir Joseph to sponsor the Royal Institution; but the basic idea was advocated by a native American who had parleyed his way in America, the Continent, and Great Britain until he reached a position of importance so that he could get a hearing. He was shrewd enough to know that he could not establish his idea without outstanding support from top British circles and he was wise enough to hit upon Sir Joseph Banks who had the influence to give the project a start and yet keep it free from politics.

The idea was first propounded in a meeting of a small group of men in the house of Sir Joseph Banks in Soho Square. This American, born Benjamin Thompson, now wore the title of Count Rumford.

A summary of Thompson's career is pertinent to an understanding of how he was able to bring his Royal Institution into successful action.

Thompson was born in 1752, in a place called Rumford, which was sometimes in the Province of Massachusetts, and sometimes in New Hampshire due to border disputes. Finally in New Hampshire, the place was called Concord. Thompson's father died when Benjamin was three, and the mother married again. Thereafter, the boy was on his own, except that he had a small inheritance from his grandfather which enabled him to attend several schools, including occasional classes at Harvard.

Like other young men among the science pioneers, he had an insatiable curiosity in the realm of the observed phenomena. For several months in his teens, he had boarded with Dr. John Hay, and from him he learned something of anatomy, chemistry, materia medica, and physics. At the age of eighteen, he began teaching at several country schools when he was called to be headmaster at a school in Concord, New Hampshire. Shortly before he was twenty, he married a wealthy widow about ten years his senior, and thus became one of the first citizens of Concord.

Thompson soon curried favor with Governor Wentworth of New Hampshire, who in 1773 gave him a commission as Major in a provincial regiment. That commission was the cause of future trouble; since the Governor was an officer of the Crown, it was assumed that his friends were Loyalists, adherents to British rule. To be suspected of such a tendency was dangerous in the temper of the times, for the ferment of colonial resentment against edicts from the home ministry was becoming explosive. There were, of course, various Loyalists in the Colonies, but they were in the minority, especially in New England.

Thompson was haled before a committee of citizens in Concord and charged with being "unfriendly to the cause of liberty." He was acquitted, but became a marked man. One day, a mob surrounded his house in Concord, but he managed to escape to his mother's home which was fifty miles away, near Boston, Massachusetts. By this time, his wife had given birth to a daughter, Sarah, and the two soon joined him at his mother's home.

Here again, a local committee charged him with being hostile to the "sons of liberty." Though he was acquitted again, his situation was increasingly precarious, for in April 1775 came the Battle of Lexington, followed by Bunker Hill in June.

There was now open warfare between the Colonies and England. Thompson, interested primarily in science, had no zeal to take part on either side. He saw no solution to his problems except to leave the country. "I have done nothing with any design to injure my countrymen, and cannot any longer bear to be treated in this barbarous manner by them," he wrote to his father-in-law. Toward the end of 1775, the Governor of Massachusetts requested Thompson to take some dispatches to England, and he jumped at the chance.

Thompson clearly had an extraordinary personality, and he soon made a position for himself in the upper echelons of the British Government and society.

While visiting at Bath in the autumn of 1777, he had made some experiments on the cohesive strength of different substances. He communicated his results to Sir Joseph Banks, President of the Royal Society, and in 1778, at the age of twenty-five, was elected a fellow of the Society. Only James Macie (Smithson) was younger when taken into membership at the age of 22, in 1787.

Thompson was appointed to the staff of Lord George Germaine, Secretary for the Colonies, who was in charge of the British military operations in America.

Thompson occupied himself primarily with tests of gunpowder and new methods for determining the velocity of projectiles. He submitted a lengthy paper on this subject to the Royal Society in 1781, which was published in its *Philosophical Transactions*.

For a brief time after the surrender of Cornwallis, Germaine sent Thompson to South Carolina to carry on the war against Colonial forces there. He took part in a few skirmishes which had no important results, for even the Home Government soon recognized that the British defeat was final.

Thompson, however, had made important changes in the designs of various types of ordnance. King George III knighted him for these discoveries, and the King of Bavaria, who was dissatisfied with his own military establishment, requested that Thompson be loaned to him. George III consented.

Benjamin Thompson, now Sir Benjamin, became the *de facto* military chief of the Bavarian forces. He made such impressive improvements in their strategy and in the design of their weapons, that the King of Bavaria desired to confer a title on Thompson. He held that men of such eminence in the European scene should have an official rank. Thompson should be Count Something-or-Other—but what? Thompson had no estate in England or Bavaria. He reflected that his origins were in Rumford. Both his mother and his wife owned properties in the general area. Hence, "Count

Rumford" was decided on. "Rumford" had the advantage that neither in England nor in the Continent would anyone know or care what his American heritage might be.

Rumford began to be homesick for England and the many friends he had there. The Bavarian monarch offered to name him as Ambassador to Great Britain. George III declined on the grounds that since the man was still a British subject, he could not, as the representative of a foreign power, meet the King on equal footing.

Rumford desired to return to England, anyhow, and he was settled in Brompton Row by early 1795, in no official capacity. Here he continued a series of studies on the efficient use of heat, and he designed a fireplace of a type which is still in use in the Western world. He became an authority on the subject of friction.

Meanwhile, he had traveled extensively in Germany and Italy, keeping in touch with such scientists as Volta and Sir Charles Blagden (also abroad at that time).

Rumford's restless mind now was studying the subject of social reform. In Munich, he had created an establishment for the poor along the lines of what would be called a social settlement today. For the poor he arranged to provide clothing at a discount, food at low prices; and he established classes in mechanics and other subjects where the working people could improve their skills.

Rumford's thoughts now began to turn to America, and he wrote to a friend there to inquire whether he would be welcome. "You could hardly conceive the heartfelt satisfaction it would give me to pay a visit to my native country." In 1796, he wrote to the Honorable John Adams, President of the American Academy of Arts and Sciences at Boston (next oldest scientific society to that of Philadelphia), offering a fund to establish a biennial medal for useful discoveries. He at once donated five thousand dollars. This was more than adequate, for by 1870 the fund had grown to thirty-seven thousand dollars. Significantly, this correspondence with the American scientific fraternity, in which the Adams family was a powerful influence, opened up an avenue of communication.

When the bequest of James Smithson was ultimately received by the United States, John Quincy Adams was the chief figure in Congress who appointed himself a watchdog to see that the fund was neither wasted nor used for frivolous purposes.

In 1797, Rumford began to develop a program for a new society in England which would apply science to useful means and establish soup kitchens and other social benefits for the poor, similar to the Munich establishment. He drew up a prospectus for such a plan and sent copies to Adams and to other heads of welfare groups in America.

The life of Rumford has been given here in considerable detail because it is typical of Anglo-American relationships in this period. The war of the American Revolution was essentially a civil war. The Colonials considered themselves to be Englishmen for many years before the Declaration of Independence. They kept petitioning the Government for equal treatment as Englishmen. But the discrimination had reached such a point that the Colonies had decided that no further petition would bring redress. Even after the formation of the United States of America the ties remained close between the Yankees and the Englishmen in the old country. Witness the fact that Rumford, even though he had fought against America and had been part of the Tory Government, was nevertheless at liberty to go back to his native land, did not hestitate to give support to the welfare activities of John Quincy Adams, and in turn was offered certain positions in the American Government. Also, the fact that he had various of the same friends on the Continent as did Smithson marked him as a cosmopolite.

The plan that had been laid before Sir Joseph was conceived in the interest of the common man. That too indicated the social consciousness of his generation as contrasted with the old school attitude of special privilege.

The rapid progress of the Royal Institution was due in part to the zeal of various persons such as Rumford and also to the fact that the Proprietors kept control of the Institution and were frequently ready to meet further assessments for special purposes. The initiation fee was a minimum of sixty guineas, as previously mentioned, but a Proprietor could subscribe up to eighty guineas.

The responsibilities of the Proprietors took two forms: Managers and Visitors. At any given time there were fewer than ten in each category but the posts were rotated. Rumford started out as a Manager and was the *de facto* boss of the enterprise for several years. As in most societies, the owners were glad to have someone who would do the major part of the work.

In order to attract additional support, provision was made for various classes of subscribers. Life memberships were sold to those willing to pay twenty guineas or ten guineas according to their preference. More than two hundred and fifty life members were enlisted in the first two or three years. This class had no voting rights but had the privilege of admission to all activities.

A third class was that of annual subscribers at two guineas each. There were eleven hundred of these. The schedule obviously was successful, for the total amount raised in the first twelve months was more than twenty-four thousand pounds.

The first move was to acquire a house at 21 Albemarle Street for the sum of four thousand eight hundred and fifty pounds. The Managers promptly remodeled the house to create a lecture room which would seat nine hundred persons. They bought adjacent buildings and established a laboratory with apparatus and a supply of chemicals. The initial report on the improvements suggested that the apparatus should be acquired bit by bit in order that it be kept up to date. Also, the Managers proposed to provide "an additional collection of books for the reference of scientific men." The total of these initial improvements came to twenty-four thousand pounds.

Referring to the purpose of the Royal Institution, it must be noted that Rumford's Munich idea of soup kitchens and reduced clothing prices had not been welcomed by the British elite. Emphasis now was on the diffusion of knowledge and the availability of scientific research for any who had the brains to embrace the opportunity. One of the initial steps was to build a chemical laboratory which would be used by any accredited scientist. Hitherto Smithson and others had been obliged to rely upon the patronage of such a man as Cavendish or supply their own equipment. The laboratories at 21 Albemarle Street, though crude by modern standards, were the best obtainable for that era. Sir Humphry Davy did his laboratory work there, and later Faraday did also.

The creation of a library therefore became the next major project. It was suggested that the Proprietors and others should provide two thousand pounds to provide books and adequate quarters for them. Within ten days the sum of twenty-four hundred pounds was raised.

This project was an epoch-making move in the creation of scientific books. There had been various elaborate scientific researches by committees of Parliament and the Privy Council. The committees made their reports available to the Parliament and Council; but, curiously, they were merely received and filed, with no plan for printing or otherwise publishing them.

The Royal Institution made a start on its library by collecting scientific articles from the various journals. Also, the Institution established its own printing press which could be used for either making copies or publishing original works. The membership list, now in the Sutro Library at San Francisco, was printed by the Institution's press.

The initial public activities of the Institution included a series of public lectures which were enormously popular. It also provided various courses in mechanics, whereby industrial workers could improve their skills. This activity also was warmly supported by many of the workers. However, some of the Proprietors looked upon that project as undesirable. The objection was that if the workers became too skilled they would become discontented and no longer look up to their superiors. Hence that part of the enterprise gradually faded out.

This interference with one of Rumford's pet schemes greatly

perturbed him. There were other details in which he found that he did not have an absolutely free hand. Hence, after the first several years, he withdrew, but he had established such a momentum that the Institution grew and endured.

The Visitors referred to earlier had the function of critics with the right to deplore or applaud. Their approval in these early years was exceptional. Their report to the annual meeting of May 20, 1803 said, "The fabric of the Royal Institution is now complete . . . upon a scale of such magnitude and with a degree of excellence that are not equaled by the efforts of any individuals in any other country, or period, of the world."

CHAPTER 10

The Name of "Smithsonite"

We hope that the name "smithsonite" will not meet with any opposition as it recalls the name of a scientist to whom we owe several important accomplishments in a time when the science of chemistry had made but few advances.

F. S. Beudant in *Traité Élémentaire de Minéralogie,* Verdière, Paris, 1832.

The above tribute to Smithson was made by a French scientist only three years after the death of James Smithson, and about thirty years after he had established his identification of zinc oxide. Clearly his discovery had made an impression on the scientific world.

Beudant, however, was apprehensive, since jealousy sometimes soured the dispositions of the young scientists. A new material world was being revealed. There was keen competition to be first in any discovery which might be a passport to enduring fame. Such an attitude was known among certain of Smithson's colleagues.

An extreme case was William Hyde Wollaston, a year younger than Smithson and admitted to the Royal Society only several years later, in 1793. Wollaston had a secret laboratory. Only he was allowed in it under any circumstances. Here he developed the isolation of the newly recognized metal, platinum, and also the processes of extracting it from the ore on a commercial basis.

Wollaston's secrecy did not protect him from challenge. Another Royal Society member, Richard Chenevix admitted in 1801, and a friend of Smithson, contended that he, not Wollaston, was the first to discover platinum. He failed to establish that claim, but was consoled by being acknowledged as being the first man to identify mercury and to be a pioneer in its uses. Chenevix remained a member of the Royal Society until his death in 1830, the same year in which Smithson died. Sir Davies Gilbert at a Society meeting, paid them a joint eulogy in which he said that the two men had been friends since college days. That was an error, for Chenevix was nine years younger than Smithson and had been educated at the University of Dublin. However, the two had been friends for many years in London and also on the Continent.

Gilbert may have been thinking of a contumacious scientist who had been at Pembroke at the same time as Smithson, to wit and namely, William Higgins, a pioneer in propounding the atomic theory. This man had challenged the good faith of John Dalton, alleging that his own work had been the first in the atomic field. In fact, Higgins was a perennial grouser. His colleagues recognized his abilities by electing him to the Royal Society in 1806, but Higgins declined to appear for induction.

It is not surprising that Beudant worried lest there be opposition to his proposed honor to Smithson, especially from the English quarter; but that did not develop. In contrast to some of his contemporaries such as Wollaston Smithson made no secret of his methods. He published repeatedly in scientific journals. He exchanged information and mineral specimens with scientists in Britain and many other countries. As mentioned earlier, he believed that modern science was so new that no one man could compass it.

Also, he was consistently generous to his contemporaries, especially those working in his own speciality of mineralogy. Of Baron Cronstedt he commented, "the greatest mineralogist who has yet appeared." The Frenchman Abbe Haüy he described as "so justly celebrated for his great knowledge in chrystallography, mineralogy, etc." This was especially tactful because Smithson's experi-

Zinc Carbonate

This mineral was named in honor of its discoverer, James Smithson, distinguished English chemist and mineralogist and founder of the Smithsonian Institution.

Despite the primitive chemical apparatus and crude reagents which Smithson had to use, he was able to achieve analytical results of the most creditable character and to enlarge our knowledge of many mineral species.

Before his time zinc carbonate and zinc silicate were confused as a single mineral species under the name "calamine", but his researches distinguished between the two minerals which are now known as smithsonite and hemimorphite.

ments with calamine were a direct refutation of the Abbe's theories that the calamines were all of one species. Smithson was gracious even to Klaproth from Hamburg, referring to him as "the celebrated Mr. Klaproth to whom nearly every department of chemistry is under numerous and great obligations."

Smithson added a new dimension to the knowledge of metallurgy when he discovered in the English countryside certain ore deposits that he was able to identify as zinc oxide. That doubtless gave him satisfaction. Further, for a man of his temperament, he would have found still more reward if he could have foreseen that products related to his discovery have been a notable contribution to the health of mankind. Zinc ointment and calamine lotion are universal household medicaments.

Zinc oxide is made today synthetically by a vaporizing process in which any zinc-bearing ore may be used. The calamine is a zinc oxide with ferric oxide added. James Smithson's original identification, however, is widely recognized as basically important. Says Leonard Chavkin, Director of Research and Development Laboratories of Bristol-Myers Company:

Smithson must have discovered and identified a zinc ore which was particularly rich in zinc carbonate. This crude material was the source of the original calamine in Europe and still is used by the British.

Calamine lotion, as the average housewife knows, can be used for the relief of mosquito bites (takes out sting), for "athlete's foot," and for various complexion troubles.

For standard medical uses of zinc oxide remedies we quote the *Manual of Pharmacology* by Torald Sollman, published in 1957: "The oxide, carbonate and *calamine* (a native zinc carbonate) are employed extensively in dermatology as mildly antiseptic and astringent protective and sedative applications in inflammatory skin diseases and on superficial skin wounds."

To return to Smithson's original discovery, in 1801 Smithson was engaged in the study of various types of calamines which occurred in several well known areas, both in Europe and in England. He was preparing to provide a paper on the subject for a meeting of the Royal Society in November, 1802. A *Manual of Mineralogy* by James Dwight Dana refers to Smithson's identification as occurring in 1803. That date may have marked the time his identification of the product became generally known; but Smithson's paper issued in 1802 referred to his diggings in Derbyshire and Somersetshire, and it was in these locations where he came upon the ores which led him to his new analysis of this type of rock.

The word calamine has been variously used through the ages. In its theoretically pure form it is identical with zinc, but neither it nor zinc exists in pure form because of the affinity of that metal for various alloys. Accordingly, there are various forms of calamine affiliated with other alloys, depending upon where the deposits are found.

Zinc is a relative newcomer among the known metals. It was originally noted as a part of the composition of bronze and was not independently recognized. The "cadmia" referred to by Pliny is thought to have been a calamine, and the present word appears in Agricola in the form "calamus," meaning a reed, in allusion to the slender stalactites characteristic of the formation of calamine. The native ores referred to by the early Latins were silicates, carbonates and oxides.

By the year 1800, various scientists had recognized that there were differences in calamines found one place or another; but proof was lacking as to the composition of those differences. Smithson, in the paper which he contributed to the *Philosophical Transactions* in 1802, had been inspired by the differences in the zinc ores which he had found in Derbyshire and Somersetshire. The Derbyshire ore was usually light grey, buff, or pale yellow. That from Somersetshire in the Mendip Hills had a brown surface but a greenish-yellow interior. When scraped by a knife it broke down into a white powder.*

* The definitions of *Smithsonite, calamines,* and *alloys* vary considerably between British terminology and that of the United States; see, for example, the dictionaries of the two countries. This chapter has aimed to satisfy the various views. Where the conflict is seemingly irreconcilable, the decision is based on Smithson's own definition reflecting the view in his times and also his report on calamines in the *Philosophical*

As Smithson used the term calamine he meant a specimen of any zinc-bearing ore. His report covered about a dozen different specimens, including the two English sources referred to, a specimen from the mines of Bleyberg in Carinthia, one from Freiberg in Germany, and elsewhere in Europe. A sample from Hungary was an electrical calamine, so called because it gave off electric reactions when in the proximity of a compass or any instrument having a free-moving metal needle. This electric characteristic is believed to be due to having a special type of crystals in its composition. (Electrical calamines are also found in the U.S.A., notably in deposits at Phoenixville and Friedensville, Pennsylvania.)

Smithson, like his fellow scientists, was obliged to carry on research with the most primitive equipment and procedure, much of it designed by himself. The blowpipe was a familiar instrument, however, available to everyone in the period, and Smithson used it on virtually every type of ore, finding that it was useful in discovering how various ore samples differed in color and behavior under varying degrees of heat. Since he usually dealt with very small samples, he had the habit of using a covered tobacco pipe as a miniature furnace. He used a variety of liquids in treatment of the specimens, such as water, carbonic acid, and vitriolic acid.

He was fully aware of the imperfection of the methods available, and frequently repeated the same experiment, not reaching a conclusion unless it had been reconfirmed many times.

In breaking down a piece of ore into its components, Smithson occasionally applied a fusibility test. His remarks suggest that this may have been his method in separating the zinc oxides from the other forms of zinc alloys. In a letter to a scientific journal he wrote, "the unequal fusibility of two substances may probably, on some occasions, be ascertained; and serve from deficiency of a better, as a means of distinction between them."

By whatever method, he separated the zinc oxides successfully; and thus he became the recognized forerunner of its applications.

Transactions. Those interested in modern comment, may refer to two books mentioned in this chapter, namely, *Manual of Pharmacology* by Torald Sollman, published in 1957, and *Manual of Mineralogy* by James Dwight Dana.

CHAPTER 11

Tremendous Trifles

All things bright and beautiful
All creatures great and small
All things wise and wonderful
The Lord God made them all.

Words by C. F. ALEXANDER
Music by W. H. MONK

These words and music by persons who were born in the era of the Young Scientists were expressive of the changing attitude of the times. They mirrored the attitude of James Smithson on the nature of the composition of this earth and the wonder of its details when he entered into his epic controversy with Granville Penn, whose fundamentalist view was that man must accept the creation of the world in six days literally as revealed in the book of *Genesis*.

The followers of Granville Penn and his school were prone to denounce any who disagreed with them as ungodly. Smithson was both a practical scientist and a devout Christian. He had been drilled in the Scriptures in his Pembroke days and he saw nothing inconsistent in them vis-à-vis the discoveries of science.

That conflict, G. Penn vs. J. Smithson, will be presented in a later chapter, but Smithson's method throughout his career was consistent with his stand in that famous debate. In this chapter are presented Smithson's account of a lady's tear and his procedure in the making of an improved and economical pot of coffee.

He knew that both might be considered trivial subjects for a serious scientist, but he regarded these experiments as tremendous trifles, for in his view, nothing in the material world was trivial. He said in one of his papers, "The particle and the planet are subject to the same laws; and what is learned upon the one will be known on the other."

Like the scientist Dr. Wollaston, Smithson believed in the manipulation and analysis of small quantities. This practice promised more secure control of the material, for there was less chance that extraneous elements would be included in small samples than in larger samples—particularly in view of the crude apparatus of the times.

Sir Davies Gilbert, in a eulogy after the death of Smithson, seemingly regarded the episode of the lady's tear as significant in Smithson's work because Smithson was fond of referring to it. Gilbert said, "Mr. Smithson frequently repeated an occurrence with much pleasure and exultation, as exceeding anything that could be brought into competition with it; and this must apologize for my introducing what might otherwise be deemed an anecdote too light and trifling on such an occasion as the present.

"Mr. Smithson declared that happening to observe a tear gliding down a lady's cheek, he endeavored to catch it on a crystal vessel; that one-half of the drop escaped, but having preserved the other half he submitted it to reagents, and detected what was then called microcosmic salt, with muriate of soda, and, I think, three or four more saline substances, held in solution."

The record does not say how Smithson caught the lady in the act of weeping at a time when he had a crystal vessel conveniently at hand. Perhaps he had insulted her or slapped her on the face in the cause of science.

The causation of tears as well as the composition of the fluid is a complex matter. It is curious that infants shed no tears until the fourth or fifth month, in spite of their ability to yell lustily; but from then on tears may be caused by pain, frustration, irritation of the eyes, or drugs.

One of the most modern medical studies on the production of tears was aided by a London Metropolitan Police Force who provided tear gas to activate the eye fluid of the patients in the experiment.

Smithson has not been regarded as a pioneer in the physiology of tears but his experiment was a forecast of what a tremendous trifle the eye fluid proved to be even in modern times. Smithson identified several saline substances, whereas one modern medical analysis produced the following tabulation of the content of eye fluid.

Substance	*Percentage*
Total solids	1.8
Ash	1.05
Total protein	0.669
Albumin	0.394
Globulin	0.275
Nonprotein nitrogen	0.051
Total nitrogen	0.158
Urea	0.04
Sugar	0.065
Na_2O	0.6
K_2O	0.14
NH_3	0.003
Chlorine	0.394
NaCl	0.65

The list clearly includes matter which was introduced in the eye fluid from the outside as well as that in the lubricant itself. The tabulation is from the book *Physiology of the Eye, Clinical Application,* by Francis Heed Adler, M.D., one of the chief authorities in the world on the clinical treatment of the eye. Presumably that report should be definitive, for the book was published as late as 1950 and devoted eight pages to the subject of tears, their composition, secretion, elimination, and so on. Dr. Adler himself, however, is not resting on his 1950 observation, but writes, "I am getting out another edition of my book and putting the new material in it."

There have been various new studies on the physiology of tears. Dr. Adler has referred us to four studies:

Balik, J.   Secretion of Inorganic Phosphorus in Tears. *Amer. Jour. Ophth.* 49; 941–945, 1960.

Brunish, R.   Protein Components of Human Tears. *AMA Arch. Ophth.* 57; 554–556, 1957.

Erickson, O.   Albumins in Lacrimal Protein Patterns. *Stanford Med. Bull.* 14; 124–125, 1956.

Giardini, A. and Roberts, J.   Concentration of Glucose and Total Chloride in Tears. *Brit. Jour. Ophth.* 34; 737–743, 1950.

Obviously the end of the subject has not yet been reached. For even latter day scientists report that some of their findings are as yet inconclusive.

The subject of the lady's tear has been dwelt upon here as illustrating Smithson's belief that a study of "the particle" may lead to tremendous reaches of inquiry.

Another principle of James Smithson was that science has an obligation to serve mankind, and he regarded his study on an improved way of making coffee to be highly important, for he said, "In all cases means of economy tend to augment and diffuse comforts and happiness they bring within the reach of the many what wasteful proceedings confine to the few."

Smithson's method of making coffee was comparable to a vacuum-drip process of modern times, and especially similar to the vacuum process used in present-day restaurants. However, he was obliged to use the simple equipment available to him. He took a small glass phial, placed coffee in it, and inserted a cork loosely. He placed the phial in a pan of boiling water so that the heated air in the vessel would be driven out. He poured in cold water on the coffee and made the cork secure so that the interior was partially a vacuum.

He then said, "By allowing the coffee to cool in the closed vessel, it may be filtered through paper, then returned into the closed vessel, and heated again, and thus had of the most perfect clearness without any foreign addition to it, by which coffee is impaired. The liquors may be kept for any length of time at a boiling heat, in private families, coffee houses, etc., so as to be ready at the very instant called for."

He held that this method was practical under the simplest circumstances. "It will likewise prove of no small conveniency to travellers who have neither kettle, nor coffeepot, nor teapot, in places where these articles are not to be procured, as a bottle will supply them." He was assuming here that the traveller would have some filter material readily at hand. He contended that this method produced coffee with a minimum of waste, and observed, "In the present instance, the importance of economy is particularly great, since it is applied to matters of high price, which constitute one of the daily meals of a large portion of the population of the earth."

The method of making coffee at that time was simply by boiling, a process in which there was considerable waste, as much of the beverage was lost in the vapor which was blown away.

Smithson's method was described in a paper which he wrote for Thompson's *Annals of Philosophy* Vol. XXII; New Series, Vol. VI, 1823.

This was only one of a variety of experiments which he made on subjects applicable to daily living. For example, he studied a small fragment from the tomb of King Psammis—brought to him from Egypt by a friend. This piece was painted with a design which had the colors white, red, black and blue. He found that the white was carbonate of lime. The red was oxide of iron. The black was pounded wood charcoal and the blue was an oxide of copper.

"Many years ago," he wrote, "I examined the blue glass with which was painted a small figure of Isis, brought to me from Egypt by a relation of mine, and found its colouring matter to be copper.

"I am informed that a fine blue glass cannot at present be obtained by means of copper. What its advantages would be above that from cobalt, it is for artists to decide."

Smithson's intellectual curiosity was endless. A lesson which may be learned from his career is that everything in the material world is worthy of study. The very catholicity of his view kept him from concentrating on any particular field. But his example served to enhance his reputation in his own time, and his studies gave hints which were useful to future research chemists.

CHAPTER 12

Prisoner of War

In August 1807, the pacific James Smithson became, to his great surprise, a prisoner of the Danish Government.

He was a victim of the hysteria which may burst forth in any country in time of war. Anyone is likely to be suspected as an enemy alien, and certainly the wanderings of Smithson had a suspicious look.

He had returned to the Continent on another of his explorations, gathering mineral specimens. He was a lone wolf as he went over the countryside, bearing with him a portable chemical laboratory of sorts and a cabinet in which he collected various specimens of rock. No wonder that there were natives everywhere who looked upon him as a sinister character.

The victories of Napoleon had made the French the dictators of most of Europe. England was an enemy to France and the French allies. Smithson was clearly a Britisher, both in appearance and in speech. It will be recalled that both he and Banks had proclaimed that science is international, but the separate nations did not necessarily act on that principle. The alliances of the various governments were continually shifting. In 1807 Denmark had joined a coalition supporting Napoleon and against England. A British fleet had sailed into the harbor of Copenhagen, which was the signal for open war between the two countries.

Even Smithson became aware that the situation was tense, and he decided to return to England. In August 1807, he had reached the little port town of Tonningen, looking for passage home. There he was seized by the Danes and jailed as a "prisoner of war." He was not charged as a criminal, in which case he could have been tried and acquitted (or executed); but as a war prisoner he would be held presumably for the duration unless he were exchanged. Since Smithson was a civilian, the likelihood of the military taking any special interest in him was slight. Obviously his incarceration was unjust, but there was plenty of evidence of his snooping around the countryside, and there was no urgency on the part of the Danish Government to give him an opportunity to prove his innocence.

Tonningen was located in the midst of a swampy area and had a damp and dismal climate. According to a letter which Smithson wrote to Banks, he had reason to complain not only of the dampness and unwholesomeness of the climate, but also of the rough treatment accorded to English prisoners. "The vigorous manner in which the English were treated and which occasioned the death of several, threw me into a state of dangerous illness and brought on a spitting of blood."

Smithson was not the only scientist to suffer as a war prisoner. William Cadell, an English geologist, was thrown into a French jail under circumstances somewhat similar to Smithson's. As early as April 1807 he had written from Paris to a London friend, Robert Ferguson, "My mind has been occupied by a great desire of leaving this country." He had been traveling in France for four and a half years (he had independent wealth) studying mathematics, chemistry, and "other branches of natural knowledge." He now sought an appointment at the Royal Institution, and thought that Sir Joseph Banks might write a letter of approval that would enable Cadell to leave France without suspicion of being a spy. Cadell's caution, however, came too late. Shortly after this letter he was apprehended and held in a French prison for several years.

There were various scientific prisoners held in what were

known as English parole towns in France. These men were kept in limited custody, having given their word not to indulge in hostilities. They were not treated as military prisoners, but they were not free to travel. These men included Blumenbach, Villers, and Viborg. All of them were known to Banks and all appealed to him for relief; but months passed before there was any action. The tactful Sir Joseph usually worked quietly, and whatever part he may have had in the ultimate release of these men is not known.

Week by week Smithson's condition grew worse. "My breast being thought in the greatest danger, my physicians were all of opinion that my life depended on my immediately quitting the Danish territory, whose air and climate are highly prejudicial to all strangers whatever."

Evidently the fame of Smithson had become known to the Danish authorities, for he was allowed to have attending physicians and was being regarded with some respect. At any rate, the King of Denmark took notice of his case and gave him a passport to leave the country.

The problem of how Smithson could manage to get back to England, even though he was now free, was difficult of solution in his state of illness.

The French ruled the area and prudence required that he clear his case with them, specifically with the French minister to Hamburg who *de facto* was the current ruler of the city. The prospect of clearance for Smithson appeared good, as he was acquainted with an English merchant named Thornton, in Hamburg, who had handled numerous matters for the British Government. Thornton in fact made overtures to Smithson saying that he was an intimate friend of de Bourrienne, the French minister. On being assured by Thornton that everything would be taken care of satisfactorily Smithson moved to Hamburg, with his spirits much improved.

M. de Bourrienne received Smithson graciously, and said that Smithson might "stay in the town in perfect safety and quiet." The young scientist of course did not wish to stay in the town, but the promise that he would be unmolested was welcome, as it would give time for him to recover his health; and further negotiations might lead to his release.

The minister, on his part, had reason to be pleased, for thanks to Thornton he had bagged a real prize. Whereas the King of Denmark had recognized Smithson as a man of distinction and had let him go, by the same token the French minister could boast of having an important British citizen in his power. The Hamburg station was a dull one with little activity, and here M. de Bourrienne had an opportunity to show to the great Napoleon that he could be just as tough as the next one. As Smithson left this seemingly reassuring interview he was seized by two gendarmes and thrown into jail. What was worse, his two captors remained in the same quarters with him, day and night. He was at all times under surveillance.

Meanwhile Thornton had faded from the scene and never came near Smithson again. Just why the English merchant who had received various favors from his home government should betray one of his countrymen is not wholly clear. Possibly he believed that Napoleon was all-powerful and would remain so. Hence it might be advantageous to be on record as a friend of the Court.

Ironically the internationalist Smithson was treated as though he had been a villain of the worst sort. The two gendarmes delighted in persecuting him. For six weeks he was not allowed to go outdoors. He was still ill and spitting blood. Even though he was in no shape to travel even under favorable circumstances they threatened to drag him as a prisoner to Verdun where he would be confined again. He had previously dreamed of getting away to the south of France where the warm sunshine might aid his recovery but, as he wrote to Banks, "I have totally lost all inclination to stay among the French."

He had been born in France, his early days were spent there, he himself had lived there intermittently and his friends among the French scientists were civilized men and a credit to an elite society in the best sense of that term. Smithson in his later years returned to association with that group but at present the thought of being a prisoner in France was intolerable. His captors painted the prospect to him in darkest terms, indicating that he would be worse off once he were incarcerated in the heart of enemy country.

Months passed by without relief and he wrote to Banks, "I am really here in a most untoward situation, in fact an utter stranger to everybody, deserted by those on whom I had depended, not perhaps to say worse, and vibrating between existence and the tomb."

The situation was indeed desperate and he might not have survived but for the unforeseen intervention of Richard Varick. Like Thornton, Varick was a great English merchant, but of a quite different character. From some source he had heard of Smithson's plight, possibly from Banks, since Smithson had been a prisoner for many months before Varick was aware of his existence. At any rate Varick protested indignantly to the authorities at this outrageous treatment and guaranteed his own person and property as a surety that Smithson would not leave the territory of Hamburg. Hence the guard was removed, Smithson was allowed to take an occasional walk and get "a little air when my strength and state of health will allow of my doing so," but he remained a prisoner.

Another improvement in his condition was the fact that he was now able to receive mail, whereas he had been virtually incommunicado. His bankers, the Messrs. Hoare of Fleet Street, London, had his address and were able to forward various communications to him, including scientific journals. One of these was entitled the *Philosophical Magazine*. Its December 1807 issue contained an article advocating a "National Museum of Natural History."

The project was similar in certain features to the recent Royal Institution and to the much later Smithsonian Institution in Washington. Namely, it urged the systematic presentation of natural objects as an important field of knowledge and it emphasized the desirability of such an enterprise being on a national basis.

The author was J. S. Duncan. He did not identify himself as John Shute Duncan, keeper of the Ashmolean Museum at Oxford (the oldest in England, established in 1682), but his evident familiarity with the whole state of museum practice in England at the time led to the general assumption that he was the Ashmolean official.

(The appearance of the article in the *Philosophical Magazine* gave weight to it. The magazine had no connection with the *Transactions* of the Royal Society, but it had been founded in 1797 by an Alexander Tilloch, himself a natural scientist, whose list of contributors were men of authority in their respective scientific fields.)

Duncan, however, was in a difficult spot. His proposed National Museum would be partially in competition with the Royal Institution. Further, the idea might be opposed by the stalwarts of the anti-science clergy who had important influence in Parliament.

The article is of interest not only because it makes placating reference to Sir Joseph Banks and others of Smithson's close associates, but also because it reflects the early difficulties of the young scientists vis-à-vis the description of the creation of the world in the book of Genesis. The clergy in general, though not all, sensed a threat to their security and their faith when these young men took it upon themselves to make independent examinations of natural phenomena, whereas the fundamentalists held that all the answers were to be found in the Scripture.

Duncan tried to forestall such opposition by saying that he proposed "a methodical display of that instructive order and harmony which the wise Author of all being has been pleased to manifest through all His works," and to instill in the public "a conviction of the all-disposing, all-prevailing wisdom, power, and glory of the omnipresent Deity."

For those who might think the British Museum adequate for his purpose, Duncan observed, truthfully, "but a small part of the British Museum is dedicated to objects of natural history." In fact, the British Museum did not establish its natural science branch at South Kensington until 1880.

Duncan tried to bolster the respectability of his cause among scientists by mentioning eminent scientific men of his day: Sir Joseph Banks, Davy, Kirwan, etc.; but that availed nothing. Duncan's efforts were blocked by two forces—on the one hand, the disapproving conservatives; on the other, the growing Royal Institution which went much further in espousal of physical science through laboratory experiments, field work, public lectures, and a vigorous membership. Nevertheless, Duncan had lent an important, if timid, voice to the new era.

There was much confusion about the dominant philosophy of the new era, depending upon what powers seemed to be in the ascendant at any particular time. James Smithson had found that his prediction of the day of wrath in which republicanism would triumph over the royal system had not come to pass.

"Equality is abolished in France," as he now expressed it. The rise of Napoleon with his conquests over the continent of Europe had intoxicated the French people with glory. They felt themselves to be a master race, though they did not use that term. The First Consul became Emperor and instituted a system of honors created by him. His favorite henchmen became dukes, marquises, barons, and so forth, depending upon the degree of service which they rendered to the new dispensation.

Napoleon also desired to include titles of the old regime to lend prestige to his peerage. That idea ran into difficulties. For example, Lafayette, who could boast a marquisate under the old regime declined the new proposed honors saying that if he wanted to claim an exalted title, he already had one. He had rejoiced in the designation of Citizen Lafayette and would continue to do so. Nevertheless the royalty system, if one may call it that, caught on, and the French people who had so recently guillotined many of the old aristocracy now welcomed a new set.

Smithson, poor devil, knowing the changed tenor of the times, hoped that a declaration of his rank would impress the authorities who were holding him prisoner. He told them that his mother was an heiress of the Hungerfords of Studley and a great niece to the Duke of Somerset. Apparently Smithson had been quiescent about the fact of his parentage during his mother's lifetime; but since her death, as he wrote to Banks, "I make little mistery [sic] of my being brother to the present Duke of Northumberland and Lord

Beverley." The present Duke was of course the oldest son of Smithson's father, and Lord Beverley was the name of a younger brother. That was an honor which had descended to the younger son by designation of the original Northumberland, who had had several titles in his portfolio.

Unfortunately for Smithson his declaration of rank made no impression. In a more stable society mutual recognition of degrees of eminence was usual. Currently, however, the power aristocracy created by Napoleon had more prestige than the ancient titles of bygone days. The titles of the English had no prestige at all, for it was only a question of time, in the French view, until Napoleon made the English a subject people. Invasion plans were already under way. Hence Smithson remained in captivity in Hamburg.

He tried not to be idle and did work on some papers; but he wrote to Banks, "You will readily believe that under such circumstances I have not been able to do much for Science. . . . I have collected a considerable mass of detached notes and observations and I have besides with me many of the papers of two more considerable works on which I have been long engaged. I wish much to get to England to arrange and finish them as I should be sorry that they were all lost by my death after all the pains and time they have cost me."

James did get back to England after all and escaped the death which seemed probable if he had been held indefinitely in Hamburg where the damp and chilly climate might have a fatal effect on anyone with consumptive tendencies.

The year 1812, it will be recalled, was the time of Napoleon's catastrophic invasion of Russia and the ruinous retreat of his armies—the beginning of his end, actually.

In that year Smithson made his escape and returned to England. It is recorded that he published two papers in British scientific journals in the year 1813. For the next decade he lived now in England and again in France (after Napoleon had fallen). His health continued to be poor and his activities relatively quiet until, in 1823, he rose to challenge the fundamentalists who sought to destroy the credibility of the young scientists.

CHAPTER 13

Smithson, Champion for Science

It may seem curious to the modern reader to find James Smithson needing to contend that Noah's Ark did not land ultimately in England and deposit the bones of his animal passengers in the Kirkdale Cave of Yorkshire, England. Yet, the pro-Noah theory had been advanced in the *Journal of the Royal Institution of Great Britain*.

The magazine, in fact, bore the more lordly title of *Journal of Literature, Science, and the Arts*. It never lived up to the boast. Rumford, Dr. Thomas Young and Sir Humphry Davy were titular editors during the earlier issues; but apparently they merely lent their names and some staff man did the work. The paper never achieved the prestige of *Philosophical Transactions*. Indeed, it appeared only intermittently. Nevertheless, anything published in it might be thought to have the backing of the Royal Institution and that distressed Smithson.

The occasion of this debate was the discovery of the Kirkdale Cave of Yorkshire, which contained the bones of hyenas, rhinoceri, a tiger, hippopotami, an elephant common to Asia, as well as water rats of a local species. How did they get there? By way of the Ark, surmised a certain Granville Penn in pages of the *Journal*.

Granville Penn was a man of considerable wealth and influence. He was the younger brother of John Penn, a charter member of the Royal Institution and a devotee of the natural sciences. The brothers were grandsons of William Penn, proprietor of the American colony of Pennsylvania until it became a commonwealth. Granville lived in the estate of Stoke Park, Bucks; and the so-called Pennsylvania Castle in Portland, England, was part of his inheritance. He had great expectations, for with the death of his brother he would inherit the revenues from the erstwhile province of Pennsylvania. Obviously, the sovereign powers of the Penn family over Pennsylvania had ceased after the success of the American Revolution, but the continuing receipts from real estate and other commercial sources were substantial. In short, the voice of Granville Penn could not be ignored.

Granville Penn was a popular literary figure. The mainstay of his reputation was his defense of the literal acceptance of the Bible as a direct and final statement by the Almighty. Penn also delved intensely into the various sources of the King James version of the Bible, and he revised certain portions which he contended had departed from the original manuscripts. He had a fluent command of Hebrew, Latin, and Greek, and made various translations of the Greek classics. His works were widely published in England and in other countries.

Penn had attended Magdalen College, and had obtained a knowledge of geology which enabled him to use technical language which gave force to his interpretation of the Scriptures. His most famous work was *A Comparative Estimate of the Mineral and Mosaical Geologies*. To the skeptical, the idea of Moses as a geologist was somewhat surprising, but Penn contended that the Biblical account of the creation of the world, as it appeared in Genesis, and the subsequent story of the great flood, generally referred to as the Deluge, constituted the true geology of the world we live in.

He recognized the existence of "mineral geology," which described the world in terms of location of minerals in different parts of the world and in various layers of the earth's crust. Penn contended, however, that the observation of those physical facts was only an incomplete description of our world. Conversely, the Mosaic version accounted for all aspects of Creation, including mankind and all other forms of life.

In support of the Noah story, Penn pointed out, accurately, that accounts of the great flood had appeared in the histories of various races inhabiting the whole area of Palestine, Asia, Persia, in fact, of all those peoples who had a recorded history.

Though Penn's book on the Mosaic theory as against that of the mineral geologists, was enthusiastically received by orthodox churchmen and others who had reason or desire to defend the literal interpretation of the Bible, Penn had little success in gaining the attention of the acknowledged scientists of the day until the discovery of the Kirkdale Cave.

The Kirkdale Cave, located in Yorkshire, had been unknown for centuries because its entrance had been blocked by gravel, grasses, and underbrush. Some workmen about the year 1800 had discovered the opening in the cave and noted the presence of bones in it. They gossiped about the fact in neighboring pubs. There had been a local epidemic among cattle in recent years and it was generally assumed that animals had gone into the cave to die.

However, rumor persisted that there were unusual bones in the cave. Various scientists came to visit it, including William Buckland, vice-president of the Geological Society of London. Buckland found, under the muddy floor of the cave, a vast collection of bones quite different from those which appeared on the surface. It was he who was able to identify the jaws of hyenas, an elephant, and the various animals mentioned above.

As none of these species was extant in England in the nineteenth century, or in the time of English recorded history, the presence of the bones was indeed a mystery. Buckland had several theories. One was that the area had once been a vast lake, that the climate of the country had once been much warmer, or that possibly a miscellany of animals from a warmer climate had been brought to England on a tidal wave.

There still remained the question of how bones of huge animals came to be found in a cave which had an entrance so small that a man had to bend down to get into it. Buckland had a theory on that score. In the cave were several jaws of hyenas. According to him, hyenas were very fond of bones in their diet. He surmised that a pack of hyenas might have made their headquarters in the cave, roamed the countryside killing other animals, then broke up the carcasses and dragged them piecemeal into the cave for further enjoyment. Buckland read his conclusions before the Geological Society of London on February 21, 1822. The paper was published in *Philosophical Transactions* of that year. Another plausible theory was that the entrance to the cave was originally much larger.

Granville Penn leaped eagerly to the conclusion that some of the animals from Noah's time had been swept into the cave, and he published these conclusions in a *Supplement to the Compara-tive Estimate*. This was a sequel to his book on Moses as a mineralogist.

The *Journal of the Royal Institution* for January, 1824, con-tained a review of the *Supplement,* summarizing Mr. Penn's view that the content of mud in the cave could have come from the subsiding waters of the Deluge. Penn also held that the bodies of the drowned animals "by putrefying, evolved a great quantity of gas which, expanding in the mud, generated the cave." Penn's earlier work on the comparison of mineral and Mosaic geologies had not drawn the attention of Smithson, but this latest theory was much too much.

Smithson was aware of the fact that if no reply were made to Granville Penn, the man's position might gain increased belief with the public and in the halls of Parliament. The danger of punitive measures being adopted against the young scientists were real. The subject had tremendous emotional content. For the next hundred years scientists were persecuted for their views. One need only mention the fury that raged about Darwin's theory of evolu-tion. In the United States, there were many instances of clergy and teachers being dismissed from their posts because they lent support to that doctrine. In Princeton, Rev. Charles W. Shields, an alumnus of the University (the class of 1844), gave a course on "The Harmony of Science and Revealed Religion." The course was continued until 1903; but it was never a part of the regular curriculum and it was supported by the gifts of private individuals. Dr. Shields had married into leading Princeton family connections.

Nevertheless, in a procedure which could have ruined the career of a less powerful man, Dr. Shields was dismissed from the local Presbytery. The excuse was that he had consented to a petition for a liquor license (the proprietor needed the signatures of all persons living within two hundred feet of his proposed store).

Grover Cleveland, a former President of the United States, signed the same petition. The Episcopalians, who seemingly had no prejudice against liquor, ordained Dr. Shields, and the University stood by him.

Such incidents were not unusual. One needs only to recall the Scopes trial in Tennessee where a teacher was "accused" of expounding evolution to his classes, and that was as late as 1924. Smithson was not exaggerating the dangers when he stood forth to challenge Granville Penn.

The question was what medium to use. As a founding member, he had every right to present his arguments in the pages of the *Journal* of the Royal Institution; but the bias of the editor was so evident that whatever James wrote might be handled in a distorted fashion. He decided to lay his case before readers of the *Annals of Philosophy*. This was a popular scientific journal, independent, and not attached to any society. In the issue of June 10, 1824, Smithson stated his case at length. There is space here for only his major points.

He agreed that a large portion of mankind accepted the Bible as from divine inspiration; that the universal Deluge was recorded there; that it was natural for believers to attribute many or all of present-day phenomena to the action of that Deluge. However, he felt that such views had not obtained "the general assent of the learned."

Smithson attacked in detail the geological theories of Penn as to the action of different minerals and the supposed effect of gas. Smithson then went on to explode the theory that the Ark could have been brought from Palestine by a sea which would necessarily have been most tempestuous to have overtopped the Alps, and brought the Ark to England.

Smithson pointed out that the Bible does not refer to such hurricanes or swollen billows assumed by Mr. Penn, nor could any vessel have survived in such an agitated sea.

Smithson went over the Biblical story in detail to prove that the theory of the Ark having been floated to England was preposterous, if one accepts the literal truth of the Noah story as Mr. Penn did. If the earth had been spread over by a deep layer of mire, Noah and the animals could not have landed upon it, or if they had tried, they would have sunk into it and been smothered. The Bible reports that Noah, after the return of the Ark on a certain occasion, became drunk with wine. If the whole earth had been covered in the manner supposed by Penn, the planting of grapevines and their coming to maturity would have taken so much time that Noah would have had to wait many years before he could get a flagon of wine.

Smithson alleged that "two great facts" completely invalidated the Penn hypothesis. One was the total absence in the fossil world of all remains of every vestige of *man himself* and his arts. Furthermore, if the Deluge had come as far as England, "human bodies by the millions must then have covered the waters . . . and human bones be consequently met with everywhere, blended with those of the animals."

He also added that the objects of human industry would have survived, "the dog would have retained his collar, the horse his bit and harness, the ox his yoke." There were a multitude of material things such as harps, pipe organs, objects of wrought iron, and bronze, which should have survived.

The evidence of marine life at great altitudes was explained by Smithson as having occurred through the eruption of volcanoes. Such a phenomenon seemed to him more believable than the supposed elevation of the sea. He complimented Mr. Penn on his effort to collate the Biblical account with the "great book of nature," but he opined that "the result has not been what was anticipated." He concluded that the story of Noah, including the promise of the rainbow that such a disaster would never be visited upon the world again, told of a miracle, and that there are no natural means adequate to explain it.

To the modern mind, Smithson's critique of Granville Penn's book was devastating. Mr. Penn, however, got in a last word, because he published a second edition of his book in which he reiterated his beliefs in great detail. He explained the absence of human skeletons and the lack of material objects as due to the possibility that human beings and their civilization were buried so deep that the evidence might now be below the bottom of the sea.

Granville Penn, however, did not win his argument for scientific proof by diving to the bottom of the sea, for Smithson returned to a simple affirmation of faith in the Biblical story.

"To collate the revered volume with the great book of nature, and show in their agreement one author to both, was an undertaking worthy of the union of piety and science. If the result has not been what was anticipated; if we look in vain over the face of our globe for those mighty impressions of an universal deluge, which reason tells us that it must have produced and left behind itself, to some cause as out of the natural course of things as was that event, must this doubtless be attributed . . . to a miracle then which swept away all that could recall that day of death when 'the windows of heaven were opened' upon mankind, must we refer what no natural means are adequate to explain."

CHAPTER 14

Paris Bound

After the controversy with Granville Penn, Smithson retired from the active arena of London and spent a large part of his time in Paris.

He was not well, and found the climate of France more agreeable. Further, the French scientists of his acquaintance had a friendliness and a graciousness which won his admiration.

There was, for example, Gay-Lussac, who literally was giving his life to science, for he was dying as the result of a wound received in his laboratory. He was younger than Smithson by thirteen years, but that did not interfere with their compatibility. Chemistry was Gay-Lussac's particular field. He was professor of physics and chemistry at the Ecole Polytechnique. He lived for many years in lingering ill health, and his last words considering his wound have become immortal. "It's too bad to be departing in this way," said he, "it's beginning to be a joke." (*"C'est dommage de s'en aller: ça commence à devenir drôle."*)

Smithson's friend Arago, was there, and we shall return to him later. Chenevix, James' friend of many years' standing, was frequently in Paris. Chenevix was famous for his observations in mineralogical systems and he became virtually a Frenchman himself when he married the Countess of Renault.

Smithson, of course, had many ties with his birthplace. He occupied a home at 121 Rue Montmartre, and some of the family fortune was invested in the Hotel Hungerford, Rue Caumartin, Paris.

Smithson's brother, Henry L. Dickinson, had sold his Army commission and returned to Paris where he lived until his death in 1820. He left his entire property to Smithson with the proviso that Dickinson's son, now using the name Henry James Hungerford, should have a life interest in the estate. The fact that Dickinson left all his property to his brother, James Smithson, has suggested to some that this bequest might account for the bulk of Smithson's wealth. However, virtually all of the property that Dickinson had, had come to him from Smithson, who had received it from his mother's properties in the first place.

Henry Dickinson had had an affair with a woman named Mrs. Mary Ann Coates. There is no record of a marriage, but she gave him the only son that he acknowledged. He left nothing to her directly, though he instructed their son to provide her with an ample allowance. She had married and had had children by her next husband, a Frenchman named Théodore de la Batut.

Henry, James' nephew, called himself Hungerford as late as 1826, but ultimately he adopted his stepfather's name, Batut, and in due course called himself Baron Eunice de la Batut.

Smithson's business transactions involved him in Paris. Also, he lent various sums of money to a servant named Sailly, who was acting as manager of the Hungerford Hotel. Smithson paid good attention to his estate, for he invested substantial amounts in French five-percent notes and British consols (interest-bearing government bonds). This kept his assets fluid, in contrast to his earlier inheritance of real estate.

In Paris, in order to divert his mind from ill health and worries, Smithson developed the habit of gambling. Some of his friends, notably Arago, were fearful lest he dissipate his wealth at the card tables.

Both in England and in France, the gambling fever was much in the air, and many men of promise were financially ruined at the gaming tables. For example, a notable member of Parliament, Charles James Fox, was saved from financial ruin only because his debts periodically were paid by his wealthy father, Lord Holland. The devotion of Arago to Smithson was a heart-warming phenomenon and a tribute to Smithson, for Arago was many years younger than the British scientist and was busy pursuing a career of his own.

François Jean Dominique Arago was born in 1786, which made him twenty-one years younger than Smithson. He was a brilliant chemist; a colleague with Gay-Lussac in editing a monthly journal of science; and at the age of twenty-three, he was voted a member of the French Academy of Sciences. As this French group was a fraternity of kindred spirits, Arago knew of Smithson's habits and observed that his life was regularly divided between the most interesting scientific researches and gaming. "It was a source of great regret to me," he wrote a friend, "that this learned experimentalist should devote half of so valuable a life to a course so little in harmony with an intellect whose wonderful powers called forth the admiration of the world around him."

To correct the habits of an older and distinguished man was delicate, but Arago was able to convince Smithson that the mathematical chances of winning were all against the player, that any gambling house sets up tables where the percentages are in favor of the house over and above the initial charge of ten percent which was taken by the proprietor of any gaming establishment.

Arago evidently was persuasive, and his approach through the presentation of mathematics carried the day. In short, Smithson agreed to put a limit on his gambling, promising to stop any time when his losses exceeded a figure that he could afford. He evidently lived up to that resolution, for his fortune when his will was probated, amounted to approximately one hundred and six thousand pounds.

Smithson did not promise to give up gambling entirely. The amusement of the sport and the gay atmosphere of the casinos was a good therapy for him. He was now in his late middle age. He was not addicted to alcohol or women. His major delight was in the pleasures of the laboratory. Research science always has a thrill of adventure for the temperament that has a bent in that direction. In the late eighteenth and the early nineteenth centuries, moreover, the scientists had the excitement of being pioneers of discovery in the new aspects of the material world.

Smithson stuck to his major calling and his enjoyment in it is manifest in the volume of work that he turned out in the early 1800's, and in the happy phrases that frequently salted his published papers. For example, in a report on fibrous copper, he said, "these fibres of copper are produced by a process entirely the same as that employed for the manufactory [sic] of macaroni and vermicelli; and which are made by forcing paste through small apertures by the pressure of a syringe." Changing the metaphor, he added, "it is wire-drawing performed inversely—by propulsion instead of traction."

In another paper, he told how he had become inadvertently the artist of a small painting. The tongue appears to be well in the cheek here, though the underlying facts are stated unequivocally. He told of desiring to transport a crayon portrait for a long distance (possibly overseas, though Smithson cannily did not specify). The main problem was to fix the colors; hence Smithson called in an expert. The latter advocated brushing the portrait with milk, but James felt that this idea was so foolish that he declined to try it. It could ruin the portrait, and all would be lost. Smithson himself thought of several solutions which he rejected as impractical. He then decided to spray the back of the picture with a quick-drying oil diluted with turpentine. He used this fluid on the back of the portrait. He then alleged, "After a day or two, when this was grown dry, I spread a coat of the mixture over the front of the picture, and my crayon drawing became an oil painting."

This anecdote appeared in the form of a letter to the editors in the *Annals of Philosophy* (Volume XXVI, New Series Volume X, 1825, page 236). Smithson, at this period, submitted most of his contributions to this magazine. He had selected that magazine as a place in which to reply to the theories of Granville Penn and he submitted most of his later papers to it (the *Philosophical Transactions* of the Royal Society were suited to more formal papers).

The *Annals* was a vigorous and original magazine, not committed to any one school of thought. The Editor was Thomas Thomson, born in 1773, Doctor of Medicine at Edinburgh in 1799. He wrote a history of the Royal Society in 1812, having been elected a fellow of that Society in 1811. Smithson was safe in those editorial hands. He continued to write voluminously on a wide range of subjects, and he was an asset to Thomson, who needed distinguished writers. Smithson, in turn, welcomed the platform of a sympathetic and distinguished journal for the expression of his new ideas. These were by no means frivolous. On one occasion he told of a conversation which he and Ampère had in Paris, concerning the behavior of melted tin which penetrated through a surrounding core of cast iron. This seemed to Smithson to confirm other experiments which he had made of capillary attraction. The comment is less important intrinsically than the fact that it is dated at Paris in February 1821, and reveals the intimacy of Ampère and Smithson.

One further experiment by Smithson deserves mention at this time because it was reported by him in 1817 to the Royal Society, and because it prophetically raised the question of why grass is green.

Or again, why is the violet violet in color, or why is the corn poppy red? It was the late Charles F. Kettering, head of the laboratories at Dayton, Ohio, U.S.A., who asked repeatedly, "Why is grass green?" Out of that grew the numerous speculations about chlorophyll and its supposedly life-bearing essence of green. The point here is not what answer Mr. Kettering may have found, but the fact that in 1817 James Smithson directed the Royal Society of London to the question: why is the violet violet, the red cabbage red, the black cherry black, or the mulberry purple? These speculations appeared in *Philosophical Transactions*, Volume CVIII, for December 18, 1818—and must have been regarded by many as subversive. Whereas the humors of a chemical test tube might yield various weird results, the inquiry into the redness of the red poppy was sticking one's nose into the chemical decisions of the Almighty. The experiments were upsetting, for Smithson proved by the application of certain acids and other fluids that the violet could be turned to green or yellow; and the rose, so red the rose?, could be changed to blue.

From the viewpoint of such a person as the vocal Granville Penn, it was time that such a man as Smithson should be debarred from putting the works of the Deity under the scrutiny of the test tube and the blowpipe. The issue did not come to that sharp a conflict, but Smithson felt that the burdens of time and doubt were pressing him hard, and in October, 1826, he returned to London to write his will.

CHAPTER 15

At Rest in Genoa

There were two significant aspects to the signing of the will of James Smithson.

One was the fact that he signed the document in lodgings in Bentinck Street rather than in the town house in Fitzroy Square which had been left him by his mother. The other was that he left his estate in the first instance to whatever blood descendant might survive him, whether legitimate or not.

The nature of the estate proved to be unusual. When the assets were totaled, they did not include the town house or any form of realty, even though his mother's will had listed considerable buildings and land. That was the usual form of private wealth in England; yet, as mentioned earlier, Smithson clearly had converted all of his holdings into the liquid form of stocks and bonds. Specifically, he proposed in the event that no blood descendant survived him, to leave his property *to the United States of America to found at Washington under the name of the Smithsonian Institution an establishment for the increase & diffusion of knowledge among men.* He foresaw the possibility of transferring his wealth across the seas, to establish a Smithsonian Institution. That dream may have been in being for some time; for to convert real property into cash, without suffering loss, is a gradual process.

Understandably, Smithson's first hope was to bequeath his for-

A page from the ledger of James Smithson's estate as recorded in the Drummond Bank, England

Excerpt from the will of Elizabeth Macie

tune to some descendant who would establish the family name. In his mother and his father there was genius. That quality had been demonstrated in his own career. The spark might recur in a future child, but the prospects for the birth of a successor were not encouraging. His brother and his brother's son were the only persons who could have carried on the line. The brother was deceased and Smithson himself was sixty-one, and not likely to marry. That left the nephew, who had not married and seemingly was not likely to. The nephew, in short, was a wastrel, living for his pleasures, which did not, however, include women. Under the circumstances, it was more than probable that the Smithson money would become available for his great design.

Meanwhile, there was the remainder of James' life to be lived. He was sixty-one at the signing of the will, October 23, 1826, a document written in his own hand. He was in command of his mental faculties, but in steadily declining health. For these later years, he chose to live not in Paris, but in Genoa. Genoa was the nearest approach to a republic that existed in the Continent of Europe. Italy was composed of numerous independent principalities, similar in language and people, but frequently quarreling among themselves, and in some cases even ruled by monarchs from other lands.

Genoa, since the days of Andrea Doria, had been self-contained. The city was located on a great harbor, the largest on the Mediterranean. It was ruled by a group of merchant princes who formed an oligarchy. They in turn chose a ruler from among themselves, called the Doge, but the office was not hereditary, nor was there any power given to the leader to create a class of nobles.

This trading center created great wealth for a dozen or more families. They lived in magnificent palaces, many of which are used now by the University, the municipality, and for other public purposes.

The existence of such wealth was inevitably a temptation to other powers. Over the centuries, first one king and then another captured the city and established a nominal rule over it, but no such attempt was permanently successful; for the natives would not accept the idea of monarchy, and had no desire to establish a king from among themselves. One of the features which served to perpetuate the oligarchy was the idea of public service. Today there is a vast hall, in the erstwhile Palazzo San Giorgio, which contains statues and portraits of leaders from the past who were distinguished for various types of benefactions, such as public parks, improved wages, advancement of medicine, better streets and highways.

The city was built on a number of hills and the streets come right down to the waterfront. The villas on the slopes and crests of the hills afforded excellent views of the dramatic terrain and the open sea. The climate was somewhat comparable to England, though far sunnier, never excessively cold in winter, and in summer almost tropical.

Many Englishmen had homes there, either year-round or for the winter season. Some were able to get a foothold as merchants or bankers, and a few married into the oligarchy. Some, like Lord Byron, visited there for long periods because of the attraction of the climate.

The inventory of Smithson's possessions indicate that he lived in style in Genoa, even as he had in Florence. He had his horse and carriage, his silver, a large wardrobe, several rings, jeweled pins and clasps, two boxes of medals, coins, and jewels, a telescope, and currency and stock from various nations. He had bank deposits with Messrs. Gibbs and Company, British bankers who had an establishment in Genoa, and various accounts at the Drummond bank in London. Most of the details of where he resided and how he occupied his time have been erased by the succession of wars which have destroyed the city records.

Most devastating was the bombardment of the city in World War II. The Germans had taken possession of Genoa from the landward side with little difficulty. It was their only free harbor of any size, and of great importance strategically. The Germans held all of the land fortifications for miles around and the only way that

the Allied forces could drive the Germans out was from the sea
and by the air. The damage was appalling.

The chief thing that is known of Smithson's life in Genoa is that
he was a devout attendant of the Church of the Holy Ghost, which
was the formal name of the English church. The church records of
the time were kept in the current building, but in World War II,
a bomb made a direct hit on the roof of the church and the records
were reduced to powder.

Toward the beginning of the twentieth century, the Regents of
the Smithsonian Institution caused a bronze plaque to be placed
on a wall of the English church commemorating the fact that
Smithson had worshiped there.

Smithson died at two o'clock in the morning on June 27, 1829.
Two brief reports remain to tell of the event. One is a report to
the Superintendent of the British Consular Service.

I think it my duty to inform you that a Mr. James Smithson died
in this city on the 27th June last.

Messrs. Gibbs & Co. bankers of the deceased, acquainted Messrs.
Drummond & Co. of London of this melancholy event, as in examin-
ing the papers of the deceased, we found a receipt of his will with
Messrs. Drummond and Company.

I made an inventory of the effects and sealed the papers of the
deceased until I hear from his friends.

The above was signed by "J.B.," probably the vice-consul referred to in the following memorandum.

The other report was made by the Consulate to the Attorney
General of Genoa. After recording the event, it states:

The same day I had sent my vice-consul into the house of the
deceased in order to make necessary arrangements for the funeral ceremonies and in order to make an inventory of the property, that which
he did do in the presence of M. J. Gibbs, English agent in the city, who
was banker for the deceased. He put the papers and the most valuable
objects in boxes and a trunk on which he placed the Consular Seals,
except for the underwear and clothes of the deceased. A part of these
would have to be washed. He had, however, left these under the care

Tomb of James Smithson at the Smithsonian in Washington, D.C.

Commemorative plaque in honor of James Smithson. Episcopal Church of the Holy Ghost, Genoa, Italy

of a servant of the deceased, a person to be fully trusted; and wrote to the relatives of the deceased in order to have their instructions.

One further record of Smithson remained in Genoa. There was an English cemetery on a hill back of the lighthouse overlooking the harbor, where Smithson was buried. His usually frivolous nephew caused a memorial tomb to be erected at the site. There the remains stayed for 75 years until they were transferred to Washington, D.C., where a new tomb was provided in a chapel at the Smithsonian. (For details of this notable event, see Part III, Chapter 9.)

The nephew, the self-styled Baron, continued to travel to various places on the Continent; and in 1835, while lodging at a hotel in Pisa, he died. He had not married and he had no illegitimate children. The latter fact may be assumed, for the executors advertised widely saying that a fortune awaited for anyone who could prove to be a descendant of the nephew, and no claimant came forward. Once the Court of Chancery was satisfied that there was no heir, it notified the American Ambassador of the terms of the will, and the first steps toward carrying out Smithson's great design were under way.

PART III

THE SMITHSONIAN'S
BIRTH, GROWTH,
AND MODERN TIMES

The basic idea of James Smithson has been dynamic. The opening chapters of this book have indicated the wide reaches of his mind, how his dream has created a vast enterprise.

However, the realistic historian will know that no new enterprise is achieved without struggle. That was clearly so in regard to James Smithson's bequest. Britain cleared the money in the first step; but what would be the attitude of the United States of America, the recipient? That was indeed the major initial question.

This section will deal briefly with the early history of the founding, and then move on to the achievements and prospects of the present day.

CHAPTER 1

Birth Pangs

Andrew Jackson, President of the United States, having been advised by his State Department that a Britisher had left a fortune for supposedly commendable purposes to be used in the United States, dumped the proposal into the lap of the Congress, on December 17, 1835. These were his words:

Washington, December 17, 1835
To the Senate and House of Representatives of the
United States:

I transmit to Congress a report from the Secretary of State, accompanying copies of certain Papers relating to a bequest to the United 'at Washington an establishment under the name of the Smithsonian Institution, for the increase and diffusion of knowledge among men.' The Executive having no authority to take any steps for accepting the trust and obtaining the funds, the papers are communicated with a view to such measures as Congress may deem necessary.

ANDREW JACKSON

For Jackson, this was a hot potato. He rarely delegated any of his authority to Congress or elsewhere, but this was something strange. He was correct in surmising that many in Congress would be opposed. Jackson had had too many conflicts with the Congress to involve himself in this new problem. He does not appear again in the issue.

149

Fortunately for Smithson's dream, a knight errant appeared early, namely John Quincy Adams, congressman and former President of the United States.

The reader may recall that Adams had experience in public enterprises in this country and knowledge of similar movements in England. Count Rumford had informed him of the activities of the Royal Institution, and had contributed funds to one of Adams' pet educational projects.

Accordingly, the congressman from Massachusetts was singularly qualified to sponsor the proposal, to give it shape, and to protect it from numerous crackpot ideas which were advanced. He was named chairman of a committee of the House appointed to study the subject, and thus was closely in touch with the issue throughout the many years—eleven—in which it was debated.

Opposition developed at the outset. John C. Calhoun, the firebrand senator from South Carolina, said that he thought it "beneath the dignity of the United States to receive presents of this kind from anyone."

In fairness to South Carolina, it should be said that Calhoun's fellow senator strongly disagreed with him. In fact, Senator Joel R. Poinsett made an eloquent speech in the Senate on January 1, 1841, favoring the acceptance of the bequest, saying in part, "There can be no doubt that a national institution, such as we contemplate, having at its command an observatory, a museum containing collections of all the productions of nature, a botanic and zoological garden, and the necessary apparatus for illustrating every branch of physical science, would attract together men of learning and students from every part of our country, would open new avenues of intelligence throughout the whole of its vast extent, and would contribute largely to disseminate among the people the truths of nature and the light of science. . . .

"This bequest will enable the government to afford all necessary protection to the promotion of science and the useful arts, without the exercise of any doubtful power, by the application of the annual interest of this fund to the establishment of an observatory, the erection of suitable buildings to contain the collection, and for lecture rooms, the purchase of books and instruments, and the salaries of professors and curators.

"Specimens of natural history are rapidly accumulating. The exploring expedition has already sent home a large collection, which remains packed away in boxes in a room belonging to the Philadelphia Museum, generously loaned by the company for that purpose; and we may anticipate, from the ability and well-known zeal of the naturalists who accompanied it by order of the government, that the squadron itself, shortly expected, will return richly freighted with objects of natural history. I cannot believe that after all the labor, pains, and expense incurred in procuring them these specimens are not to be brought to Washington to be arranged and exhibited here."

Senator Poinsett himself was a talented amateur naturalist with particular interest in botany. Indeed, virtually all leaders of America were naturalists to some degree, for the United States then was predominantly an agricultural nation. Virtually every landowner or land renter grew his own vegetables and flowers, and in consequence many took a scientific interest in husbandry and related sciences.

Senator Poinsett concluded with the hope that the bequest would result in "the foundation of a National Museum and contribute to spread the light of science over our land." Nevertheless, there was strong opposition from some quarters.

Andrew Johnson, of Tennessee, the future President of the United States, entered into the discussion on two counts. He held first that the Federal Government was morally responsible for the security of the funds. On the other hand, he objected to setting up an educational institution in the city of Washington with all its "extravagance, folly, aristocracy, and corruption."

Robert Owen of Indiana, founder of the New Harmony community, pointed out that Smithson had designated Washington City as the place for the establishment of the Institution. To that, Johnson replied that he was opposed to the entire scheme.

Then Jefferson Davis, the future President of the Confederacy, asked whether Johnson would favor sending the money back to the Court of Chancery in England. Johnson said that he would.

Probably there was never any likelihood of the Congress rejecting the gift, which had an intrinsic value of several million dollars in today's terms. Many schemes were already being dreamed of in the minds of various congressmen as the debate progressed.

The senators and representatives from some of the states were not opposed, but abstained from debate. However, Massachusetts, North Carolina, New Jersey, Indiana, and New York were actively in favor. Jefferson Davis of Mississippi, F. P. Stanton of Tennessee, and Joseph R. Ingersoll of Pennsylvania supported the proposal on a final vote.

During the years of debate there were forty-one discussions in the Senate, and fifty-seven discussions in the House. Senator Rufus Choate, eloquent attorney from Massachusetts, strongly supported the cause of Mr. Adams, though his particular desire was to establish a library with the Smithson funds. Jesse Speight from Stantonsburg, North Carolina, was on the Adams Committee, though several of the "Tarheel" delegation, such as Ebenezer Pettigrew of Cool Spring, chose to remain silent. Gideon Hawley was one of the chief proponents from New York, and he became one of the initial Regents of the Smithsonian.

Senator Sam Southard of Trenton, New Jersey, undertook a reply to Calhoun, who had questioned the constitutional right of Congress to establish a national university with the Smithson funds. Southard maintained that Congress had the same right to do that as it had to charter a college in Georgetown or Alexandria.

Adams made a clinching address for acceptance of the fund in the House on January 19, 1836. The speech was extensive, but the gist of it is contained in his peroration:

Under this Government, a new experiment in the history of mankind is now drawing to the close of half a century, during which the territory and number of States in the Union have nearly doubled, while their population, wealth, and power have been multiplied more than fourfold. In the process of this experiment, they have gone through the vicissitudes of peace and war, amidst bitter and ardent party collisions, and the unceasing changes of popular elections to the legislative and executive offices, both of the general confederacy and of the separate States, without a single execution for treason, or a single proscription for a political offence.

The whole Government, under the continual superintendence of the whole people, has been holding a steady course of prosperity, unexampled in the contemporary history of other nations, not less than in the annals of ages past.

During this period, our country has been freely visited by observers from other lands, and often in no friendly spirit by travellers from the native land of Mr. Smithson. Their report of the prevailing manners, opinions, and social intercourse of the people of this Union, have exhibited no flattering or complacent pictures.

All the infirmities and vices of our civil and political condition have been conned and noted, and displayed with no forbearance of severe satirical comment to set them off; yet, after all this, a British subject, of noble birth and ample fortune, desiring to bequeath his whole estate to the purpose of increasing and diffusing knowledge throughout the whole community of civilized man, selects for the depositaries of his trust, with confidence unqualified with reserve, the Congress of the United States of America.

The motion to accept the bequest was passed during that session, and on September 14, 1836, Richard Rush wrote to the solicitors for the Drummond Bank, Messrs. Clarke, Fynmore, and Flagdate, seeking an appointment to arrange a transfer of the money.

The funds were produced, and their transfer to the United States occurred in a picturesque manner. Though Smithson had left his estate in the form of stocks and bonds, which obviously could have been transported overseas, such a procedure would have created difficulties. This was before the days of telegraph or telephone, and six weeks or more was required for the tranportation of ocean mail between England and America.

Richard Rush, accordingly, arranged for the sale of the securities and converted the proceeds into gold sovereigns (each worth one pound sterling). The sovereigns were then put into sacks, filling eleven boxes, and delivered to the United States mint at Philadelphia, where they were melted down and recoined into gold dollars. The total was over five hundred thousand dollars.

When the funds arrived in the United States and were deposited with the Secretary of the Treasury, they became promptly involved in a curious political transaction. The Treasury invested the money in securities of four states: Arkansas, Illinois, Michigan, and Ohio. The total paid for these securities was just under six hundred and one thousand dollars, in Government notes, and the supposed redemption value was six hundred and twenty thousand dollars. (Gold certificates had a higher face value than gold coin.)

Of the total distributed to the four state funds, more than five hundred and fifty thousand dollars were invested in bonds of the state of Arkansas. Why this peculiar arrangement was made was something of a mystery. Obviously, the transaction did not go unnoticed. Adams attacked the procedure on the floor of the House on two grounds: first, that the interest rate of the investment was only five and a half percent, lower than the six percent which was then normal; and secondly, that most of the bonds involved were not redeemable until 1860 or later, thus tying up the funds for an extended period if the initial investment were left undisturbed.

On April 19, 1841, Adams addressed a letter to the Secretary of the Treasury Ewing, informing him of the financial problem; and accompanying the letter was a report on the state of the prospects for the Smithsonian and other related documents. Weeks went by, and Mr. Ewing made no reply. Adams assumed that he might have taken the matter to John Tyler, the acting president (President Harrison was critically ill). Ewing retired from office without having replied to Adams's letter and by mid-September he had been succeeded by Walter Forward. Hence, Adams called upon Forward to tell him about the Smithsonian fund and to ask for a report of the debts of the several states where the money was invested. The House had passed a resolution calling for such a report from the Treasury.

Mr. Forward appeared to be ignorant of the whole matter, and presumably Ewing had not told him about this piece of unfinished business; but he promised to look into it, and to write to the several states for information. There was still more delay of several weeks, which Forward excused by saying that he had not heard from all of the states involved. Adams then went to Tyler and informed him of the state of affairs. Tyler said that in the interim he had received Adams's letter to Ewing, had read it, approved of it in general, and would cooperate in trying to get some action.

By this time, Tyler, who had become President of the United States upon the death of his predecessor, now had the unqualified weight of office at his disposal, and proceeded to use it. He sent a message to the Senate in the following words:

SENATE, December 7, 1841

Message of the President, John Tyler

. . . I suggest for your consideration the propriety of making without further delay, some specific application of the funds derived under the will of Mr. Smithson, of England, for the diffusion of knowledge; and which have, heretofore, been vested in public stocks, until such time as Congress should think proper to give them a specific direction. Nor will you, I feel confident, permit any abatement of the principal of the legacy to be made, should it turn out that the stocks, in which the investments have been made had undergone a depreciation.

As a result of the agitation, the Treasury was required to accept responsibility for the total of the original bequest and to guarantee an interest payment of six percent annually. From that time forward, there was no further attempt to raid the funds of the bequest or to apply them to the advantage of any political faction.

Finally, in 1846, a bill to establish the Smithsonian, to handle the funds, to provide a building, to establish a Board of Regents mainly from high officials of government, and to reserve the right of Congress to revise any of the provisions, was introduced by Robert Owen of Indiana.

The bill passed both houses of Congress and was signed by James K. Polk, then President of the United States, on August 10, 1846. The Smithsonian Institution at last was born.

Seal of the Smithsonian Institution

CHAPTER 2

Initial Program

Secretary Henry, an international scientist and a former professor at Princeton University, tactfully sought the opinion of a wide range of educators on a program which he had proposed for the Institution.

The emphasis was chiefly but not exclusively on various fields of science, because Henry personally had the knowledge to pass judgment on those areas. He also heeded two warnings which had arisen in the Congressional debates. One was that the fund should not be swallowed up in expensive buildings; and secondly, the various projects should not be concentrated solely in the city of Washington. On the latter point the introduction to his program stated:

"It should be recollected that mankind in general are to be benefited by the bequest, and that, therefore, all unnecessary expenditure on local objects would be a perversion of the trust."

The activities of the Smithsonian have always been worldwide. Secretary Henry deserves credit for that emphasis. In his program he stated the following principles:

TO INCREASE KNOWLEDGE. It is proposed—
1. To stimulate men of talent to make original researches, by offering suitable rewards for memoirs containing new truths; and,

157

2. To appropriate annually a portion of the income for particular researches, under the direction of suitable persons.

TO DIFFUSE KNOWLEDGE. It is proposed—

1. To publish a series of periodical reports on the progress of the different branches of knowledge; and,

2. To publish occasionally separate treatises on subjects of general interest.

In the implementation of these principles Henry recommended the study of ethnological researches, particularly with reference to the different races of men in North America; explorations of various kinds; systems of extended meteorological observations; encouragement of the fine arts; and publication of treatises on subjects of general interest.

He noted that an act of Congress establishing the Institution contemplated the establishment of a library and a museum. He strongly favored the first part and recommended the collection of various objects which would provide the nucleus for a museum, but he did not wish to expend any substantial part of the sum for an expensive musem building.

Henry's plan of organization for the Smithsonian outlining how his future work should be implemented was singularly prophetic and well worth reading in the light of what took place. The chief exception to the accuracy of his prophecy was the modesty of his expectations. He thought that a few persons could handle the job—which was true at the very beginning. His plan was as follows:

(1) The act of Congress establishing the Institution contemplated the formation of a library and a museum; and the Board of Regents, including these objects in the plan of organization, resolved to divide the income into two equal parts.

(2) One part to be appropriated to increase and diffuse knowledge by means of publications and researches, agreeable to the scheme before given. The other part to be appropriated to the formation of a library and a collection of objects of nature and of art.

(3) These two plans are not incompatible with one another.

(4) To carry out the plan before described, a library will be required, consisting, 1st, of a complete collection of the transactions and proceedings of all the learned societies in the world; 2nd, of the more important current periodical publications, and other works necessary in preparing the periodical reports.

(5) The Institution should make special collections, particularly of objects to verify its own publications.

(6) Also a collection of instruments of research in all branches of experimental science.

(7) With reference to the collection of books, other than those mentioned above, catalogues of all the different libraries in the United States should be procured, in order that the valuable books first purchased may be such as are not to be found in the United States.

(8) Also catalogues of memoirs, and of books in foreign libraries, and other materials, should be collected for rendering the Institution a center of bibliographical knowledge, whence the student may be directed to any work which he may require.

(9) It is believed that the collections in natural history will increase by donation as rapidly as the income of the Institution can make provision for their reception, and therefore, it will seldom be necessary to purchase any articles of this kind.

(10) .Attempts should be made to procure for the gallery of art casts of the most celebrated articles of ancient and modern sculpture.

(11) The arts may be encouraged by providing a room, free of expense, for the exhibition of the objects of the Art-Union and other similar societies.

(12) A small appropriation should be made annually for models of antiquities, such as those of the remains of ancient temples, etc.

(13) For the present, or until the building is fully completed, besides the Secretary, no permanent assistant will be required, except one, to act as librarian.

(14) The duty of the Secretary will be the general superintendence, with the advice of the Chancellor and other members of the establishment, of the library and scientific operations of the Institution; to give to the Regents annually an account of all of the transactions; of the memoirs which have been received for publication; of the researches which have been made; and to edit, with the assistance of the librarian, the publications of the Institution.

(15) The duty of the Assistant Secretary, acting as librarian, will be, for the present, to assist in taking charge of the collections, to select and purchase, under the direction of the Secretary and a committee of the board, books and catalogues, and to procure the information before mentioned; to give information on plans of libraries, and to assist the Secretary in editing the publications of the Institution and in the other duties of his office.

(16) The Secretary and his assistants, during the session of Congress, will be required to illustrate new discoveries in science, and to exhibit new objects of art; also distinguished individuals should be invited to give lectures on subjects of general interest.

(17) When the building is completed, and when, in accordance with the act of Congress, the charge of the National Museum is given to the Smithsonian Institution, other assistants will be required.

In the fall of 1847 Henry circulated his program to many leading educators, primarily the presidents of colleges and universities, soliciting their opinions.

One of the first responses was somewhat negative. This came from Albany Academy of which Henry, at one time, had been a professor. The current head of the school expressed distress that the subjects of medicine and surgery had not been included. He also deplored the omission of the subject of hygiene and the health of communities. He felt that the delegation of certain fields of science to particular persons on occasions might lead to "the formation of predominant cliques." However the letter concluded

The first Smithsonian building

with the desire that the Smithsonian would reach the highest usefulness and he stated "your plan as a whole has my unqualified approbation."

President Benjamin Silliman, of Yale, gave his approval together with certain conditions. He felt that Congress, having taken so long to establish the Institution, should provide some compensation, such as paying for a simple new building to house the enterprise. He took note of the fact that congressional opinion had proposed that the National Museum should be administered by the Smithsonian Institution. If this took place, Mr. Silliman proposed, Congress should bear the expense of providing requisite accommodations without taxing the Smithsonian funds. The New Jersey Historical Society passed a resolution of approval, as did the American Academy of Arts and Sciences, and also the American Philosophical Society.

Mark Hopkins, of Williams, approved, but emphasized that much must depend on the selection of competent personnel to carry out the various proposals.

Hamilton College, Pennsylvania College at Gettysburg, Wesleyan University at Middletown, Connecticut, Bowdoin College,

William and Mary, the University of North Carolina, Trinity at Hartford, and Kenyon College at Gambier, Ohio, were among those from which expressions of enthusiasm were received.

There were many famous names among the endorsers, including Edward Hitchcock of Amherst, and Francis Wayland of Brown. The chief institutions whose names do not appear on the record are Harvard and Princeton, but it is probable that Secretary Henry had consulted each in personal conference.

The success of his opinion sampling was impressive, for all replies were affirmative.

CHAPTER 3

Man's Origins

Granville Penn, who had tilted with James Smithson regarding the results of the Deluge, must have spun in his grave at one of the first research projects to be undertaken under the Smithsonian bequest.

It will be recalled that Penn contended that the explanation of all the material world was to be found in the book of Moses, but Secretary Henry disregarded that theory and proposed research into ethnology as one of the initial activities of the Smithsonian. Henry used the word in a general sense, as does the definition in the Oxford English Dictionary:

The science which treats of races and peoples and of their relations to one another, their distinctive physical and other characteristics, etc.

That gave as wide a range as one might desire and was synonymous with anthropology. The same dictionary gives three definitions of that word, which has shifted in meaning from time to time.

First: The science of man, or of mankind, in the widest sense.

Second: The science of the nature of man embracing human physiology and psychology and their mutual bearing.

Third: The 'study of man as an animal' (Latham); the branch of the science which investigates the position of man zoologically, his 'evolution' and history as a race of animated beings.

The continent of North America supplied a virgin field for the study of anthropology, for here was the locus of a race of men, of differing tribes, the American Indians, of whom little was known then from a scientific standpoint.

The very first study published by the Smithsonian was *Ancient Monuments of the Mississippi Valley* by E. George Squier and E. H. Davis, issued December 1, 1848. This was a handsome volume, illustrated by forty-eight lithograph plates and two hundred and seven wood engravings. The Smithsonian records indicate that "a copy was sent to every principal library of the world." As stated in a footnote to part I this book has been listed generally as *Smithsonian Contribution to Knowledge, Vol. I.*

Prior to this publication, Mr. Squier had made a pamphlet summary of the work undertaken by him with Davis, which was printed in New York in 1847 under the title *Observations on the Aboriginal Monuments of the Mississippi Valley.* It only pretends, however, to be an introduction to the major work, as there is an advertisement on the back cover telling that the Smithsonian will shortly publish the complete story which will consist of "not far from 500 pages of letter-press."

The first classification of numerous Indian tribes included the study of the existing Indians whose tribal ways were expected to vanish or be modified through contact with the white man's civilization.

There were some three hundred thousand Indians living on reservations, and research divided them for study on the basis of language. Amazingly, there were fifty linguistic families, comprising more than five hundred distinct Indian languages. That is to say, there might be a number of dialects within a root language.

The work was in charge of Major John W. Powell, who studied all phases of the tribes, including differences in beliefs, organization, customs, and arts. He also organized scientific studies of typical tribes in the various groups.

Oddly enough, the tribal differences were not necessarily determined by geographical location. For example, there was the

Oklahoma Seneca-Cayuga tribe, relatives of the Five Nations, but obviously located far below Cayuga's waters.

The Smithsonian inaugurated the first systematic investigation of the American Indians, and succeeding studies covered diverse peoples, so that the white man learned that it would be unscientific to think of such a thing as a typical Indian; for example, there were the peaceful Pueblos, with cultivated fields and apartment-like dwellings, the marauding Navahos and Apaches of the Southwest, the warlike Sioux, Omaha, Mandan, and other tribes of the Great Plains, the Iroquois of the Northeast, their League of Nations.

The volume of studies became so vast that in 1879 the Federal Government consolidated its surveys as the United States Geological Survey. The anthropological work thereof was placed under the direction of the Smithsonian Institution as the Bureau of American Ethnology.

The Smithsonian Bureau of American Ethnology has studied the Indians, increasing our knowledge of every phase of their lives in nearly every one of the United States, in most of the countries of South and Central America, in Mexico, and in the West Indies. During that period, many of the smaller tribes have dwindled to but a few old individuals, or have disappeared, and in some instances valuable scientific information has literally been snatched from oblivion by recording the last words of dying survivors. Indian mounds to be inundated through the construction of dams have been excavated through Smithsonian cooperation, and knowledge of them and their contents preserved for posterity.

The Bureau has seized every opportunity to get from the older Indians the authentic aboriginal rites, customs, and words that are no longer remembered by the younger generations. All through its history, the Bureau has kept in mind the vital importance of recording ethnological material that is in danger of being lost forever.

From these widespread investigations has come a stream of publications that make a sizable library of Indian lore. Bureau

An 18th century adobe dwelling from the area of Sante Fe, New Mexico. Museum of History and Technology

Heads of early American Indian types

publications have always been in great demand, not only by libraries and anthropologists, but also by the general public, for the "red man" has ever been of keen interest to all Americans.

Bureau ethnologists have obtained their information firsthand by going among the tribes to be studied and working directly with the best informants available. Often by patient diplomacy and by cultivating an understanding of the Indian mind, the investigators were given access to secret rites and ceremonies never before witnessed by white men.

Fortunately, the Indian never suffered the handicaps of having a different color skin, for that primary reason. He was referred to as "the Red Man" in contrast to the white man, though actually his complexion was approximately copper-colored. There were legends about the heroism of the so-called Red Man. James Fenimore Cooper's novels idealized him. There was a fraternal order of white men founded in 1813 called "The Improved Order of Red Men." It currently reports about ninety thousand members.

The Indian has been exploited frequently by the white invaders. He generally has been confined to reservations because of years of hostility toward the white man, resulting in massacres, but he has *not* been treated as a second-class citizen. From the beginning of the Virginia colony, the Indian was regarded with respect, thanks largely to Pocahontas. According to legend, she saved the life of Captain John Smith, who was about to be murdered by her tribe. Later she married an Englishman, the colonist John Rolfe, an interracial marriage which met with widespread approval. To the present day there has been intermarriage, one famous example being that of that of the parents of the famous Will Rogers, who was half Cherokee.

Several white Bureau staff members have been elected honorary members of certain tribes, and at least two Bureau ethnologists were themselves Indians and so had a twofold interest in the tribes they studied. In the field, language has been recorded phonetically; creation and other myths have been set down as cited by Indian informants; rites and ceremonies with all their pomp and paraphernalia have been observed and recorded. The innumerable details of customs and ways of life have been noted—marriage and birth customs, initiation and puberty rites, taboos, types of dwellings, hunting and fishing, war, sports and games, weapons, clothing, food, ornaments, and all other phases of Indian life as it was before the white man came to interrupt the development of their civilization.

In modern times there has been expansion in digging, due to the large growth in the creation of dams. The building of a dam means an excavation many feet deep, usually changing the direction of the river basin. With the removal of thousands of cubic feet of earth, all of the historic evidence that might lie only relatively few feet below the earth could be lost forever if the material were not closely examined at the time of excavation. Hence the Bureau of American Ethnology has established a unit called the River Basin Surveys that works in cooperation with the National Park Service, the Bureau of Reclamation of the Department of the Interior, the Corps of Engineers of the Department of the Army, and state and local organizations in programs for "salvage archaeology" in areas to be flooded or otherwise destroyed by the construction of large dams.

Activities in the field pertained, in large part, to surveys and excavations. Most of the work was concentrated in the digging or testing of sites, but surveys were made in six new reservoir basins. Five of the new reservoirs were in Kansas; the sixth was in Nebraska. Nine excavating parties were in the field in the Missouri basin and one survey party was operating in Montana. Digging was started in the Smith Mountain Reservoir area in southern Virginia, and a small group collected pollen samples from areas in western Nebraska.

As of June 30, 1963, archaeological surveys and excavations had been made, since the start of the salvage program, in a total of 264 reservoir areas located in 29 different states. Furthermore, two lock projects, four canal areas, and two watershed areas, had also been examined. Since 1946, when the program got under way,

5,009 sites have been located and recorded; of that number, 1,175 were recommended for excavation or limited testing. Because of the conditions under which the salvage operations need to be conducted, complete excavations, except in the case of a few small sites, are rarely possible. Consequently, when the term "excavation" is used, it generally implies that only about ten percent of a site was dug.

By the end of the year, 484 sites in 54 reservoir basins and one watershed area had been either tested or excavated to the degree where good information about them had been obtained. It has been the policy of the River Basin Surveys to dig in at least one example of the various kinds of sites reported in the preliminary surveys. The sites range in nature from those which were simple camping areas, occupied by early hunting and gathering Indians of about ten thousand years ago, to village remains left by historic Indians of the mid-nineteenth century. In addition, the remains of frontier trading posts of European origin and of Army installations also have been examined.

We have said Major John W. Powell was the pioneer in these Indian studies, but before the founding of the Bureau of American Ethnology, he had become famous as the first man to explore the Grand Canyon of the State of Colorado.

Major Powell was a veteran of the Civil War, in which he lost his right arm, but in spite of this severe handicap, he conceived and carried out the perilous plan of descending the length of the unknown Colorado in boats, for the purpose of mapping it and studying the geological structure. With ten men in four boats, each boat with watertight compartments in bow and stern, the expedition started down the canyon in May 1869.

The dangers and hardships surpassed even what Powell had anticipated. In the granite sections, rapids and falls were almost continuous and the canyon wall was precipitous. In many places portage was impossible because of sheer rock walls that rose from the water's edge, and here there was no alternative but to run the rapids. The boats were frequently swamped or overturned, but the explorers always succeeded in clinging to the sides and climbing aboard again when calmer water was reached. The courage of four of the men failed and they left the party, three of them only to be killed later by Indians. Most of the provisions were spoiled through frequent wetting; instruments and collections had to be abandoned; floods rushed down the side gorges after every rain; but Powell and the remaining men went doggedly on until at last they came out of the canyon into smooth water below, and success had been achieved.

Explorations in the West were continued in the 1870's with Major Powell in charge, and observations on the various Indian tribes encountered were considered to be a definite part of the duties of the personnel.

The Grand Canyon exploration has been mentioned here because of Powell's connection with Indian affairs, but it should be said that exploration has been and is one of the primary activities of the Smithsonian. Various examples in that field are to be found in the following chapter.

CHAPTER 4

Explorations and Canal Zone

Smithsonian explorations started almost with the founding of the Institution in 1846. These researches have explored virtually every branch of science except medicine.

An early critic of Secretary Henry's prospectus noted and deplored the omission of medicine, but the Secretary was not moved. He had indicated that his program did not contemplate competing with other institutions. In the nation, even that early, there were medical schools, laboratories, and hospitals doing medical research, and over the years there has been expansive development in private research foundations such as the Rockefeller and Sloan-Kettering Institutes. The Federal Government, also, has made contributions to medical science in the United States Public Health Service, in Walter Reed Hospital, etc.

But apart from the medical field, the exploration of the unknown has infinite possibilities. Hence, exploration has been a major activity of the Smithsonian throughout the years. That has been the chief activity in following out the first part of James Smithson's bequest to pursue "the increase of knowledge." Exploration has supplied most of the material for the contents of the various buildings under the Smithsonian administration in Washington. Millions of persons annually visit the exhibits without perhaps realizing that these are the end results of activities which have been and are being carried on all over the world.

In these days of atomic energy, electronics, jet propulsion, television, and similar spectacular scientific achievements, the public is likely to get the impression that nearly all science is material science. It should not be forgotten, however, that to achieve anything like a mastery of nature, mankind has need also of the natural sciences—biology, zoology, and anthropology—and that these sciences too, although not so often in the headlines, have made tremendous strides in recent decades. The Smithsonian Institution has had a large part during more than one hundred years in the advancement of all sciences, which have brought to man a constantly fuller knowledge of the earth and its inhabitants past and present, and of the universe. In many research areas, exploration plays an important role.

Scientific exploration has a primary purpose—the acquiring of new knowledge. An expedition may go no more than fifty miles away, or its objective may be in an untrodden jungle thousands of miles from headquarters, but the basic purpose remains the same—to acquire new information in the field, or to collect specimens for later study in the laboratory. As stated above, Smithsonian explorations started almost with the founding of the Institution in 1846. It has not sent out many large-scale expeditions; rather, the purpose of exploration has been accomplished through numerous small-scale exploring parties sent out for specific objectives. Occasionally, however, through the financial aid of friends of the Institution, large Smithsonian expeditions have taken the field with outstanding results.

A fairly accurate total of the expeditions from 1910 to 1940 may be obtained from the annual Smithsonian Exploration Pamphlets, published during that thirty-year period. These pamphlets show that the Institution sent out or took part in 709 field explorations. The preceding sixty-four years of Smithsonian history accounts for at least an equal number of expeditions—so that a total of fifteen hundred is a very conservative estimate.

Numerous Smithsonian expeditions have been sent to explore South America, Central America, the West Indies, Alaska, and, of

course, every state in the United States. Among the remote localities visited may be mentioned Antarctica, New Guinea, Borneo,
Celebes, Midway Island, Wake Island, Siam, Kashmir, Siberia,
Mongolia, the Aleutian Islands, Greenland, Algeria, Liberia, Tanganyika, Patagonia, the Galapagos Islands, and Easter Island.
Every conceivable type of terrain has been studied—high moun-
taintops and underground rivers; rugged "badlands" regions and
the endless rolling prairie; perpetually frozen Arctic sites; and
tropical atolls; desert wastes where life is virtually nonexistent;
and the rank growth of sodden rain forests. All these varied aspects
of the earth's configuration have yielded up grist for the mill of
science. Tangible evidence of Smithsonian explorations in all
parts of the globe may be seen in the exhibition and study collections of the National Museum, and in the pages of Smithsonian
publications.

The Smithsonian has had a continuing policy of cooperating
with others in field research. While in many instances it handles
every detail of an exploration, in other cases it is a collaborator
with the Government or with private institutions such as The
National Geographic Society.

In number of expeditions, biology has predominated, especially
in foreign regions, because the study of living organisms depends
very largely for "raw material" on field collections. Large biological collections came from the numerous Government surveys of
the little-known West of the 1850's, and the Smithsonian Institution had some part—large or small—in almost every one of these
important explorations. Later came the intensive exploration of
the American seacoasts, lakes, and rivers, by the Fish Commission,
a Government agency created by Congress largely through the
initiative of Spencer F. Baird, then Assistant Secretary of the
Smithsonian. Through his close association with the Commission,
the Institution took some part in these explorations and received
extensive collections as a result of them. (Further details will be
given later in this chapter.)

Probably during very few years in Smithsonian history has the

Institution failed to send out or be represented in a number of expeditions in the interests of biology. It would obviously be impossible here to attempt a full catalog of these expeditions; but we may mention a few typical ones.

In 1909, there went out the Smithsonian–Theodore Roosevelt African Expedition which brought back for the National Museum a large and unique collection of the interesting animals of the Dark Continent. On exhibition in the Museum, these animals have ever since been one of the most popular features of the Smithsonian.

In 1912, Ned Hollister represented the Institution on the Harvard Expedition to the little-known Altai Mountain region of Asia, bringing back an almost complete series of the interesting mammals and birds of that wild, desolate area.

Between 1912 and 1918, through the financial assistance of Dr. W. L. Abbott, H. C. Raven explored Borneo and Celebes, making biological collections of unusual value, filling many gaps that existed previously in the Museum collections.

Dr. Waldo L. Schmitt, working under the Institution's Walter Rathbone Bacon Traveling Scholarship, devoted most of his time in the years 1925 through 1927 to a study of the crustacean fauna of the South American continent. His explorations covered most of both coasts of that continent, and the resulting collection contained more than fifteen thousand specimens of marine life.

In 1932, through the generosity of Eldridge R. Johnson in offering the use of his two-hundred-and-eighty-foot yacht and in financing the expedition, Dr. Paul Bartsch conducted successful marine explorations in the Atlantic's greatest deep, the Puerto Rican Deep. Bottom hauls were made down to a depth of three thousand two hundred fathoms, producing extensive collections as well as many meteorological, physical, and chemical data. As stated above, these are merely arbitrarily selected examples of Smithsonian biological exploration.

The research in anthropology, especially among the American

Indians, has been discussed in another chapter. It should also be observed that Smithsonian anthropologists have led or taken part in numerous expeditions to Mexico, Central America, South America, the West Indies, Alaska (both before and after it became one of the United States), as well as more remote regions such as the East Indies, islands of the South Pacific, parts of Europe and Asia.

The number of Smithsonian geological field expeditions has been somewhat smaller than in some other subjects, doubtless because the United States Geological Survey has so ably carried on field work in this country. The Institution has, however, always been active in the fields of paleontology, mineralogy, and petrology, in all of which field work is a necessity. Best known of the Smithsonian's paleontological work in the field is that conducted for many years by Dr. Charles D. Walcott, fourth Secretary of the Institution. His researches for a long period were in the difficult field of Cambrian and pre-Cambrian geology and paleontology, and at the time of his death, one of his professional colleagues wrote to him that seventy percent of our knowledge of the ancient Cambrian life forms was due to Walcott's work. His yearly field work was done mainly in the Canadian Rockies, where he discovered many excellent outcrops of Cambrian formations and collected and described numerous new fossil genera and species.

Many small-scale expeditions have taken the field in this country to study and collect the fossil remains of creatures of past geological eras, and their success is attested by the extensive exhibition and study series in the National Museum of both vertebrate and invertebrate animals of the past. Mineralogy, also, has benefited from numerous small Smithsonian expeditions, both in this country and in foreign lands.

Perhaps the best way to provide a glimpse of the scope and variety of this phase of Smithsonian activity is to present the titles of the investigations for a single typical year as reported in the Institution's annual exploration pamphlets. The year selected as being fairly typical is 1930, and the list of field expeditions for that year is as follows:

Studying the Sun in California, Chile, and Southwest Africa

Collecting Insects in the West

Further Explorations for Mollusks in the West Indies

Pursuing Microfossils on the Atlantic Coast

Monacan Sites in Virginia

Ancient Culture of St. Lawrence Island, Alaska

Music of the Winnebago, Chippewa, and Pueblo Indians

Explorations in Szechuan, China

Continuation of the Fossil Horse Roundup on the Old Oregon Trail

Further Investigations on Evidences of Early Man in Florida

Fossil Hunting in the Bridger Basin of Wyoming

Studying the Indians of New Mexico and California

Collecting Silver Minerals in Ontario, Canada

Field Researches among the Six Nations of the Iroquois

A Botanical Visit to South and East Africa

Anthropological Work on the Kuskokwim River, Alaska

Arizona's Prehistoric Canals, from the Air

Biological Collecting on "Tin-Can Island" in the South Seas

Ancient Relatives of Living Whales

Prehistoric Santo Domingan Kitchen-Middens, Cemeteries, and Earthworks

Studies of the Cheyenne, Kickapoo, and Fox Indians

The Cruise of the *Esperanza* to Haiti

The Search for Ancient Life Forms in the Rocks of the Western United States

A Prehistoric Village on the Zuni Reservation, New Mexico

Trawling for Crustaceans at Tortugas, Florida

Mounds of the Vanished Calusa Indians of Florida

Archaeological Reconnaissance in Texas and Nevada

Indian Language Studies in Louisiana

Afield with the Birds of Northern Spain

The above tabulation of the twenty-nine expeditions may be broken down into the following subjects:

Ethnology—11
Paleontology—5
Birds; Reptiles; Insects—4
Geology—3
Biology and Botany—2
Mollusks; Crustaceans—1 each
Astrophysics—1
Archaeology—1
Anthropology—1

Ethnology has continued to lead the list largely because the River Basin excavations produced Indian relics and yielded many other artifacts. (The River Basin projects are summarized in the chapter on Indians.) The work in that category is being continued currently through the 1960's and will not terminate as long as the building of new dams creates new fields for it.

One may turn to the various Smithsonian reports of these explorations to get a sense of the drama that frequently is experienced by amateur contributors. For example, Rev. David C. Graham, a missionary in China, was an explorer in his spare time. He submitted the results—"a fine series of insects of all orders," according to the Smithsonian. In the process, he was fortunate to escape alive in his encounters with leopards and robbers. A scientist is so concentrated on his goal that he tends to overlook the personal dangers and the lack of creature comforts.

No loss of life has ever been reported due to the hazards encountered on these trips, and the Smithsonian sees to it that its expeditions are well equipped. It furnishes about three thousand two hundred different items in a year. These range from whale harpoons to specially loaded shells for collecting humming birds, certain insects, and tropical moths. The method used is to shoot at them with very fine dust.

A notable example of the cooperation by the Smithsonian with the Government and others was the establishment of the Marine Laboratory at Woods Hole, Massachusetts, which for nearly a century, has been the mecca for marine biologists from all over the nation and abroad. In this instance, the Smithsonian was not only a cooperator, but the instigator.

Assistant Secretary Baird* was especially interested in biology, including the study of fish. He learned in his summer visits to the Atlantic coast that there was an alarming decrease of edible fish. He prevailed upon Secretary Henry to allot $100 from Smithsonian funds to study the problem, and persuaded the U. S. Treasury Department to furnish a thirty-foot yacht, the *Mazeppa*. As a result, he was able to help in the drafting of the bill passed by Congress in 1871 to establish a Fish Commission and to name a Fish Commissioner to serve without additional salary to his existing work, whether he be with the Government or in outside employment. Baird was appointed and served as Commissioner in addition to his work at the Smithsonian. By June 1871, he had established headquarters for the Commission at Woods Hole.

The initial purpose was to determine the cause and cure of the decline in edible fish, but soon all phases of marine life were studied at the Woods Hole Laboratory. Ultimately, the Fish Commission ended its work there, but the activity carried on. In 1902, the American Fisheries Society placed a bronze plaque on a granite boulder "in memory of Spencer Fullerton Baird, U. S. Commissioner of Fisheries, 1871–1887." There is now a Woods Hole Oceanographic Institute which has shown its appreciation of the Smithsonian by providing three separate grants to it for special subjects in marine research.

Canal Zone Biological Area

One of the most important explorations of the world is that located on the Barro Colorado Island in the middle of Gatun Lake in Panama. As stated in the opening chapter of this book, the

* Successor to Henry as Secretary in 1878.

island is the only tropical scientific research station of its kind in the new world. It is important because of the variety of flora and fauna found there, and because the research is continuous.

This island has been administered by the Smithsonian under the direction of its sixth secretary, Alexander Wetmore, only since 1946. However, elaborate research had been carried on there, on the island and the surrounding area, since the early years of the twentieth century, by the authority of the Canal Zone headed by General Goethals. The area was intrinsically a wilderness, a bit of modern civilization had been dropped into the middle of it by the necessity to provide accommodations for those working on the construction of the Canal. There were about thirty thousand employees; hence, the operation required mammoth-scale offices, sleeping quarters, kitchens, mess halls, machine shops, coal storage plants, schools, hotels, clubs, and recreation centers. To supply the recreation center Fred Thompson, creator of Luna Park in Coney Island (and of the New York Hippodrome) built a similar amusement part in the Canal Zone. Ultimately it failed financially, but served to delight the population throughout the peak years of construction work.

The top research person in those construction years was William C. Gorgas, Surgeon General of the United States. An earlier effort by the French to build the Canal had failed, largely because of the heavy toll of illness among the workers caused by yellow fever and malaria. Gorgas addressed himself successfully to finding the, chief causes of these diseases and taking steps to eradicate them.

The publicity resulting from his work and from the construction of the Canal itself alerted the scientific fraternity to the opportunities for research in the area; and for many years, through the present time, there have been surveys of the animal and plant life of the land and waters of the Canal Zone, including insects, birds, and fishes.

There were research teams under various sponsorships including those of universities and of the Government itself. Because of this diversity of authority, it ultimately became evident that some centralized direction would be desirable, and because of its experience in scientific exploration, and its sizable staff of scientists, the Smithsonian Institution was selected by the Government.

The report of activity of one year alone, 1963, is impressive. During that year the area was visited by eighty-seven scientists, students, and observers. Many stayed for serious projects, and others were there merely to observe the wildlife of the area. In addition, there were one hundred and fifty-five day visitors.

Climate conditions in the area are continuously uncomfortable, both because of the tropical heat and rainfall, discouraging to frivolous visitors. The tabulation of annual rainfall on the island over the past forty years shows that in most years the rainfall has been well over 100 inches. It reached a peak of 143.42 inches in 1935, and recorded 140.47 inches in 1960. 1930 had the minimum rainfall of 76.57 inches. January, February, and March are the dry season with almost no rain, but from then on, precipitation rises. For example, in August 1961, there was rainfall of almost 20 inches.

As indicated, the longer-term visitors have come there with serious purpose, and they are primarily from universities, museums, and technical organizations. There have been scientists from abroad, including Norway, Sweden, and England.

The special objectives of these scientists ranged widely, including studies of Army ants, of the behavior and physiology of cockroaches (appallingly large in that area), of spiders, of bats; the recording of bird songs, and various aspects of the study of botany, insect life, bird life, fish, reptiles, and marine life. One research was in the field of limnology, namely, the scientific study of fresh waters, especially ponds and lakes, to learn their physical, chemical, and biological conditions.

During the year, the administration continued to improve the area facilities in order to make tropical living conditions more endurable. They built a new boathouse, providing additional space for launches, speedboats, and canoes. All houses were painted and their roofs repaired. New rain gutters were installed (a frequent necessity). The expansion of the library was continued.

An interesting item of the report was that two guards were hired to maintain a constant patrol of the island and "this has greatly alleviated the problem of poaching."

The long-term research of that year consisted of continued studies on the behavior of perching birds and of primates; a study of bat populations on the island; work on the structural relationships of Panamanian composite flowers; a study of the ecology, population structure, and behavior of several species of buntings, sparrows, and certain other birds of the Canal Zone and adjacent parts of the Republic of Panama.

The financing for the maintenance of the island and its living facilities comes from several sources, apart from the Smithsonian. It includes contributions from individuals, from the New York Zoological Society, from the Eastman Kodak Company, and the Kansas State University.

The National Science Foundation, also, has approved a grant to install an electric cable from the mainland to the island. This will provide a reliable and abundant supply of electric power for the laboratory, replacing the costly and deficient generators which have always been a serious problem. This improvement will permit new equipment in the laboratory, enlargement of the herbarium, and maintenance of more extensive records of scientific data.

The far-flung influence of the Canal Zone enterprise is illustrated by the reasons for the contribution by the Eastman Kodak Company, which is encouraging research in the field of tropical biology because of its relationship to the preservation of photographic film. Eastman Kodak's early interest in the tropical area arose from the problem of storing and using photographic film under high temperature and high humidity conditions. Gelatin which contained light-sensitive silver halide in photographic emulsion encouraged the growth of various fungi, especially in tropical areas. To solve this problem Kodak for some time maintained its own research laboratory in Panama, and thus contributed to the facilities on Barro Colorado Island.

CHAPTER 5

Celestial Science

Not since the Tower of Babel has mankind so audaciously explored the heavens as in the past ten years.

The world has been thrilled by the success of space travel; and the knowledge of the universe is constantly growing. An important contributor to that knowledge is the Smithsonian Astrophysical Observatory.

Man has been curious about the heavens since earliest times. Astronomy might be called the first science practiced by the ancients in early civilizations. In the United States, the leading exponent of celestial science was Samuel Pierpont Langley, third Secretary of the Smithsonian. He visioned a new era in astronomy, saying:

"The prime object in astronomy until lately has been to say *where* any heavenly body is, rather than *what* it is, but within the present generation a new branch of astronomy has arisen, which studies the heavenly bodies for what they are in themselves and in relation to ourselves. Its study of the sun, for instance, beginning with its external features, led to the inquiry as to what it was made of, and then to the finding of the unexpected relations which it bore to the earth and to our daily lives on it, the conclusion being that in a physical sense it made us and recreates us, as it were, daily, and that the knowledge of the intimate ties which unite man with it brings results of a practical and important kind which a generation ago were hardly guessed at."

The Astrophysical Observatory began its work in 1890 with headquarters in a small frame structure erected for the purpose on the Smithsonian grounds. In it, Langley constructed a spectrobolometer, which he had invented some years before, for the purpose of studying the spectrum of the invisible infrared rays of the sun, largely unknown up to that time. No attempt will be made here to describe this piece of research except to say that it was a delicate and difficult one, performed under very unfavorable conditions. It is indeed remarkable that Langley succeeded in extending the infrared spectrum to twelve times that previously known. Langley's bolometer when perfected was capable of measuring a change of temperature of one-millionth of a degree.

Other investigations were undertaken at the Observatory, including one on light without heat, in which Langley showed that processes exist for the production of such light. However, the research that eventually came to be the chief concern of the Observatory was the measurement of the intensity of the sun's radiation as it would be if observed entirely outside the earth's atmosphere. This measurement, extremely delicate and complicated, is known as the solar constant, although actually it has been found to vary considerably from day to day.

Langley, realizing that the first requisite for good solar observations was clear air, made an expedition to Mount Whitney, in California, in 1881. Here in beautifully transparent atmosphere he made numerous observations and calculated a new value for the solar constant which stood for twenty years, until further refinements in observation served to correct it and establish a new value.

After the establishment of the Astrophysical Observatory, Langley and his associates continued observations on solar radiation at Washington, although the atmosphere there was highly unsuitable. However, experience was gained and instruments were improved, and in 1905, the opportunity came to observe on Mount

Wilson, California, at the invitation of the Carnegie Institution of Washington.

The solar constant of radiation had from the beginning shown variation regardless of observing conditions, and from this time on the study and recording of this variation became a leading purpose of the work. In 1909 and 1910, observations were made at the summit of Mount Whitney, fourteen thousand five hundred feet high, and from then on Smithsonian observers have occupied observing stations on high mountain peaks in many odd corners of the earth to check the variation in the sun's heat. Observations are made regularly at three stations—Mount Montezuma, Chile; Table Mountain, California; and Burro Mountain, New Mexico.

The Astrophysical Observatory includes two divisions: the division of astrophysical research in Cambridge, Massachusetts, for the study of solar and other types of energy impinging on the earth; and the division of radiation and organisms in Washington, for the investigation of radiation as it relates directly or indirectly to biological problems. (Further comment on this will be found at the end of this chapter.) Shops are maintained in Washington for work in metals, woods, and optical electronics, and to prepare special equipment for both divisions; and a shop conducted in cooperation with Harvard College Observatory in Cambridge provides high-precision mechanical work. Twelve satellite-tracking stations are in operation—in Florida, Hawaii, and New Mexico; and abroad, in Argentina, Australia, Curaçao, India, Iran, Japan, Peru, South Africa, and Spain.

In 1955 the Observatory took a major step forward in its move to Cambridge, Massachusetts, for in that location, it was readily able to collaborate with the Harvard College Observatory. Dr. F. L. Whipple of the Harvard faculty was called to be the Director of the Smithsonian project. The two institutions occasionally embark on joint enterprises; for example, they carry on a "radio meteor project" with headquarters at Havana, Illinois.

The modern study of meteors would have fascinated James Smithson, for throughout his career he kept a cabinet of meteor specimens. He exchanged specimens with scientists in other countries when he and they had duplicates to spare.

The subject of meteors has become regarded more seriously in the past decade. Though the general public may think of the meteor as a rare object, the stratosphere is in fact constantly filled with this "sky dust." The particles vary in size from a grain of sand to several tons. Designers of satellites recognize that the meteors are a celestial traffic hazard and have recommended meteor-bumpers for the space vehicles. The pitted surface of the moon is thought to be due in part to the collision of meteors and some of the meteors which have landed on earth have been bounced off the moon.

The meteors are believed to be particles thrown off by comets. The comet Arend-Roland, which was photographed by modern cameras, was shown to have seven tails each consisting of "dust" ejected from the central body.

Though modern science knows more about meteors than the ancients, observations of the latter are still in use. It will be recalled that Halley's Comet, which appeared in the sky in 1910, appeared as predicted within the span of a few hours, based on its appearance in the sky in 1759 and 1835. It had been noted in Chinese records about the time of the birth of Christ and was perhaps the "Star in the East" mentioned by the Wise Men.

The comet Encke is believed to have been visible twenty-five hundred years ago.

Meteorites are varied in their composition; aluminum, tritium, xenon, argon, nickel, and iron are among the substances found in them.

The solar energy potentially available in desert regions of the earth is many times the entire world's present power requirement. In future years when coal and oil are not so plentiful and cheap as they are at present, this solar energy may be called upon to replace present sources of power. There are several types of solar heat collectors that convert solar energy into useful work. One type consists of cylindrical mirrors which focus the reflected sun's rays

Examples of meteorites on view at the Natural History Building

upon glass tubes. The tubes are filled with a black liquid to absorb and store the heat for solar cooking devices, or to produce steam for developing power for mechanical purposes.

When man had discovered how to make satellites, the next problem was to track their course from observation points on the earth. The solution was not simple. No existing telescope or camera was adequate. To fulfill this need the Baker-Nunn camera, the primary instrument for observation today, was developed.

There are twelve Baker-Nunn stations on the earth today. The history of the Baker-Nunn camera may seem unromantic, yet modern celestial science depends on this device.

During the spring of 1956, Dr. James Gilbert Baker of the Harvard Observatory, who was a specialist on the construction of telescopes and cameras, saw the need for a new type of camera which could photograph the satellite and follow its course. It was necessary in building such a camera not only to design the lenses but to find the proper type of glass. The optical glass was finally obtained in Germany and a proper mirror was obtained from the Corning Glass Works in Corning, New York. The manufacture of the camera was assigned to Perkin-Elmer Corporation in South Pasadena, California.

While Dr. Baker was responsible for specifying the design of the lens and mirrors, there was still the problem of designing the camera itself; in other words, the vehicle which would contain the photographic mechanism.

Joseph Nunn of South Pasadena, California, who was the nation's leading technician on astronomical devices, was the creator of this part of the design. He worked on it for most of 1956.

An additional problem was to build a vehicle which could follow the unusual course of the satellite. Like a star, the satellite rises into the sky from the horizon, culminates, and then sets. The satellite's culmination is not of course limited to the observer's meridian. Its path on the celestial sphere is not necessarily restricted to the semicircle, nor is it symmetrical about culmination. Hence, the angular velocity of the satellite as observed from a point on the surface of the earth may change greatly between horizon and culmination.

Accordingly, the traditional telescope mount, designed to track stars, would be inadequate to track satellites. The Nunn camera was set in a mounting which enabled it to be pointed in various directions geared to the predicted motion of the satellite. The speed of its adjustment is such that it could traverse the sky from horizon to horizon in ninety-three seconds. The camera photographs at rates ranging from one frame every two seconds to one frame every thirty-two seconds.

The scale model of the camera was completed in 1957 and twelve cameras were built duplicating that design. The type of film was another problem. After a series of experiments at the Agassiz Station of Harvard Observatory, the staff chose an emulsion known as ID-2. It provides the spectral distribution needed, that is, reflected sunlight, and is a faster film than any of the other emulsions then available. Some forty thousand feet of this film was ordered from Eastman Kodak Company and put in storage for tests of the camera in South Pasadena and at the New Mexico field station.

The twelve Baker-Nunn camera stations throughout the world are Organ Pass, New Mexico; Clifantsfontein, South Africa; Woomera, Australia; San Fernando, Spain; Mitaka, Japan; Naini Tal, India; Arequipa, Peru; Shiraz, Iran; Curaçao, Netherlands West Indies; Jupiter, Florida; Villa Dolores, Argentina; and Mount Haleakala, Hawaii.

Supplementing the Baker-Nunn camera stations are teams of volunteer observers who check the position of a satellite at any given time and forward the information to the Communications Center at Cambridge, Massachusetts. There are approximately a hundred of these teams throughout the world. The observers are equipped with copies of an atlas of the heavens, with a stopwatch, and with a simple telescope known as the Moonwatch monoscope. The last item had to be purchased by the individual observers, or by a sponsoring organization, local organizations or by industry sponsors such as the Seven-Up Company, a soft drink concern. The cost of such a monoscope was about fifty dollars.

The Moonwatch Program today, in spite of its titular hundred stations, has boiled down to the nucleus of the serious and continuing astronomical fans. There are various associations in this field, both national and local, including a society on the Pacific Coast. When satellites first came into being, there was a vast interest all over the world to see these man-made satellites orbiting in the heavens.

Two of the continuing stations—those of Mr. G. R. Wright of Silver Spring, Maryland, and Mr. Lawrence White of Falls Church, Virginia—are in suburbs of Washington, D.C. Each maintains a Moonwatch station near his home. Mr. Wright has his in his back yard, which has enough elevation and sky space for effective observations.

Today the Smithsonian Astrophysical Laboratory at Cambridge, Massachusetts, is still receptive to signing up volunteer watchers. (The work is all voluntary.)

Cambridge does a useful job in keeping the watchers alerted as to what they may be able to see in their areas at any given time. Once a week Cambridge mails out a list of satellites in the sky, specifying when and where they might be visible. The reentry of a satellite into the home area is most important for the local watcher. No requirement, financial or otherwise, is made of the volunteer observer, but if his records are late or patently inaccurate, he is soon dropped out of the current lists.

There are several classes of stations, depending upon abilities and equipment. The present-day requirements are simpler than those at the outset. Present-day reporters need only one monoscope. Cambridge assigns a number to each individual observer; and each station has its own number.

Though the Moonwatch procedure may seem informal, it is carried out with a high degree of faithfulness. Astronomy has always held a fascination for mankind, and in most communities there are enthusiasts who welcome the opportunity to take part in the scientific program.

Our opening chapter referred to Robert Goddard of Clark University, Worcester, Massachusetts, who outlined in 1919 a method for reaching extreme altitudes, and who later, supported in part by grants from the Smithsonian Institution, conducted a series of limited experiments to demonstrate the practicability of his ideas. Thereafter, both in the United States and in Europe, increasing attention was paid to the development of rockets for military use and for the probing of the upper atmosphere and the exploration of outer space.

The fundamental idea was that rockets of limited thrust could penetrate the upper atmosphere and bring back valuable scientific data. Later, manned rockets of greater power would reach outer space and eventually journey throughout the solar system.

The concept of an artificial satellite orbiting the earth was a fairly late development, because such a vehicle would be of little scientific value unless it could signal information back to the earth or could be tracked by orbital or other means. The idea had to await the invention of suitable telemetry and tracking techniques.

Another significant project was the creation of a star catalog. Initiated in 1959 under the Satellite Tracking Program, the Smithsonian Astrophysical Observatory Star Catalog was conceived as the compilation of a large number of fundamental and differential catalogs to cover the sky in a standard coordinate system. The project used about forty catalogs providing data on approximately a quarter of a million stars. Preparation of the Star Catalog involved investigations of the details of the coordinate system and derivation of proper motions of each catalog. Comparisons of several catalogs were also made in sky areas where the catalogs used did not provide adequate information. The complete catalog is stored on magnetic tape.

Neither the Smithsonian headquarters nor the Smithsonian Astrophysical Observatory would claim exclusive credit for the activities described in this chapter. The work is made possible through the support of many sources, such as the National Space Administration, the United States Air Force, the Atomic Energy Commission, the Enrico Fermi Institute for Nuclear Studies (University of Chicago), Harvard University, the Massachusetts Institute of Technology, and contributions from private industries.

For the diffusion of knowledge, the observatory staff have written scores of papers, appearing in various scientific journals. Further, the special reports of the Smithsonian Astrophysical Observatory are catalogs of satellite observations, orbital data, and preliminary results of data analysis prior to general publication.

Division of Radiation and Organisms

In 1929, a new type of research was inaugurated through the establishment of the Division of Radiation and Organisms. Supported at first by Smithsonian private funds and by financial aid from the Research Corporation of New York, it has since been recognized as so valuable as to merit support by the Government and is now administered as a division of the Astrophysical Observatory. The new division investigates the effects of radiation on various types and of different wave lengths on living organisms, chiefly plants.

The first few years of the division's activities were devoted to the assembling and developing of the extremely delicate and complicated instruments and apparatus needed for the research. Experiments were then begun on the effect of various types of radiation on the growth of plants, and many interesting and valuable findings have come from these experiments. Like other phases of Smithsonian research, this work is fundamental in character and is not restricted to work of an immediately practical nature. The effort is to discover basic laws and principles, in the sure knowledge that all such discoveries will eventually be put to use in promoting the welfare of mankind. It has about thirty scientists who devote their energies to experimentation, attendance at professional conferences, and publication of pamphlets.

The work of this division is virtually incomprehensible to the layman, though not less important for that reason. Its reports are studded with words unfamiliar to the general reader. For example, here are a dozen terms taken at random from a recent annual report, with an attempt to translate them into the vernacular.

ion—an electrically charged particle which results from the breaking up of molecules

macromolecules—a grouping together of simple molecules capable of independent existence

plastid—protoplasmic unit

chloroplast—an example of plastid having some functional activity

chloramphenicol—an amide in which chlorine replaces hydrogen attached to a nitrogen atom

diatom—a type of algae

pelagic—oceanic

morphological—structural

substrate—a substance acted upon, as by an enzyme

hypocotyl hook—first part of the bean to appear above ground

avena—a genus of grasses (including oats).

Many mysteries about the effect of light and dark on plant life continue to be studied, but the researches into marine life have been especially rewarding.

Marine organisms are peculiarly suitable for fundamental investigation of radiation responses; and a section was organized within the division for marine biology research. The long-term aim of this study is toward establishing an adequate understanding of the physiology and biochemistry of the occurrence, behavior, and potential harvest of marine organisms.

In the sea, algae carry out the conversion of light energy to chemical energy. Phosphorous compounds are involved and play an important part in the determination of the bulk and growth rates of the algae. A number of types of phosphorous compounds have been identified, quantitated, and used in structural studies.

Some idea of the plant studies is indicated by the following comment of the Division Chief, W. H. Klein: "Many biological responses, such as flowering, pigment synthesis, seed germination, stem elongation, and leaf expansion are controlled by photochemical reactions initiated by various portions of the visible spectrum". In a program of study never previously undertaken elsewhere, measurements of specific spectral regions of sun and sky radiation are being recorded and correlated with plant growth responses of living material produced in natural daylight and in controlled environment conditions."

CHAPTER 6

More Stately Mansions

Build thee more stately mansions, O my soul,
As the swift seasons roll!
—OLIVER WENDELL HOLMES

The world's largest and most modern exhibition hall is the Museum of History and Technology opened in 1964 by the Smithsonian. It is one of the wonders of Washington.

The late President Kennedy praised the structure for its "direct simplicity" and its "clean lines." *U. S. News and World Report* has described it as "the hottest show in Washington."

The public demand was such that soon after the initial sessions it was necessary to keep the museum open evenings to accommodate the crowds.

Among its modern features are escalators and ramps for ease of climbing, air-conditioning, special flooring to minimize "museum fatigue," and novel window arrangements to provide ample light while retaining extensive wall space.

For daylight, the building on all sides presents a series of panels jutting out at right angles to the wall. Each panel is the frame for a tall vertical window which admits daylight indirectly into the museum rooms. Since the building is air-conditioned throughout, the windows are not needed for ventilation. Hence the usual cumbersome sashwork is absent and a corresponding extra expanse of flat surface becomes available for display purposes.

194

The man initially responsible for the architecture was the late James Kellum Smith, the last surviving partner of McKim, Mead and White. The firm was noted for the excellence of its classic structures which included the Pennsylvania Station in New York, the University Club in New York, and the American Academy in Rome. It was well-known also for designing buildings which required complex engineering.

Shortly before receiving the contract for the new Smithsonian museum, the firm declined an offer to design a one-hundred-million-dollar skyscraper in New York. Smith said at the time: "Fortunately our firm is in the position where it can choose whatever projects provide the most interest for us and a skyscraper job would offer no particular challenge."

Smith's particular field in recent years had been in campus architecture. He had been the official architect for Amherst, Bowdoin and Smith Colleges among others. Accordingly, it was appropriate that his firm be appointed to design the Museum of History and Technology, an essentially educational project, and that he be the partner responsible for the job.

Affiliated with Smith were fellow architects Milton B. Steinmann and Walter O. Cain. When Smith died these two men carried on and Cain was actually the chief architect for the building.

While the structure itself has numerous interesting features, its real significance, of course, lies in its contents. Possibly the most important historical object is the original Star Spangled Banner, fifty feet high, which is displayed at the center of the building. This is the flag which flew over Fort McHenry during the bombardment of Baltimore in the War of 1812 and inspired Francis Scott Key to write the words of what is now the United States National Anthem.

The exhibits include the original gowns of the First Ladies, household furnishings and period rooms of the seventeenth, eighteenth, and nineteenth centuries, American costumes, early farm machinery, locomotives, carriages, a cable car, automobiles, clocks, phonographs, typewriters, locks, and hand and machine tools.

Also exhibited are objects associated with famous Americans

Gown worn by Mrs. John F. Kennedy at the inauguration of her husband

A satin brocade gown of the Bustle Period around 1880. Hall of American Costume

and historical events. These include the uniform of Washington; his sword and field kit; the printing press at which Franklin worked; the coat worn by Jackson at New Orleans; the desk on which Jefferson drafted the Declaration of Independence; the steering wheel of the battleship *Maine*, the only surviving gunboat of the Revolutionary War, complete with cannons and more than five hundred objects found on it when it was raised from the bottom of Lake Champlain; and other outstanding treasures from the Smithsonian collections.

Technical subjects include Morse's telegraph, Borden's evaporator, Thomson's electric welder, Howe's sewing machine, the Whitney cotton gin, the original electromagnet constructed by Joseph Henry, the earliest Bell telephone instruments with original patent models, and many other examples of American invention. There are halls devoted to the history of physics and chemistry, electricity and electronics, nuclear energy and machine tools, transportation, steam and internal combustion engines, manufactures, early farm machinery, and textiles.

Objects of the decorative arts include ceramics, glass, musical instruments, prints, printing presses, photographs and photographic equipment.

The notable collection of coins, the history of money and examples of medallic art are exhibited in the numismatics hall. The National postage stamp collection and the history of the mails, illustrated with early postal covers and models of mail coaches are here too.

Since the Smithsonian has had a dynamic growth from the outset and probably will continue to expand, the recital of exhibits in any one building is subject to change, as in the present instance.

For example, the contemplated Air Museum mentioned in the opening chapter will doubtless cause rearrangements. When and if Congress gives approval to this new structure it will indeed be another "stately mansion," for of course the plans call for a huge building.

A working model of the Eli Whitney cotton gin, made by the inventor around 1800

Benjamin Franklin's printing press

The Howe sewing machine, the first one to be patented in the United States

Early autocar, about 1901

It is an odd bit of irony that Joseph Henry desired to have but little money spent on structures, yet through the years the Smithsonian has become housed in a complex of buildings which the architect, J. K. Smith, once described as "of palace size."

Secretary Henry, of course, was quite justified, because he was initially limited to the proceeds of the original bequest of James Smithson and he believed that the bulk of the funds should not be swallowed up in a costly building.

However, Smithson's inspiration had come to a new and growing country which had a minimum of facilities. It supplied a need for some administrative organization to take care of the scientific

Early Oldsmobile, model about 1918

Inverted Center, 1918. 24¢ airmail issue. Fewer than 100 copies exist.

Inverted center. St. Lawrence Seaway commemorative issue, Canada 1959

Enlarged reproduction of the first U.S. Government stamp, issued in 1847, which is displayed on the introductory panel to the Hall of Philately and Postal History

Inverted vignettes, U.S. Postage, issue of 1869

and artistic growth of the country. Hence, supporting money poured in and has continued to do so. Congress has been the major continuing benefactor, but there have been various private bequests of great size (which will be referred to subsequently), as well as hundreds of individual contributions of small cash value, yet of historic importance.

A creative feature of this new museum is its design for usefulness. For example, there are rooms created particularly in the interests of the thousands of school children who visit Washington every year. Here classes may be held for relatively small groups, explaining in advance what the children will be seeing. The Junior League has volunteered to provide guides.

There are assembly halls which can be closed off from the rest of the museum for meetings of scientists, educators, or other groups which have reason to meet there.

Though many find statistics to be dry, it may be of interest to engineers, builders and other museum technicians to include here the dimensions of this museum as follows:

1st floor and basement	577 ft. long; 301 ft. wide
2nd, 3rd, and 4th floors	491 ft. long; 216 ft. wide
5th floor	405 ft. long; 152 ft. wide
Cooling tower	311 ft. long; 52 ft. wide
Height to parapet	77 ft. above Constitution Avenue
	59 ft. above Madison Drive
Height to top of cooling tower	109 ft. above Constitution Avenue
Volume of building	13,802,745 cu. ft.
Gross area	753,667 sq. ft.
Net area	518,818 sq. ft.
Total public area	347,760 sq. ft.

This building was conceived and born under the highest auspices. It was dedicated by President Lyndon B. Johnson on the evening of January 22, 1964. Speakers at the dedication were Chief Justice Earl Warren, who is Chancellor of the Smithsonian Institution, and Senator Clinton P. Anderson, Regent of the

Base viola da gamba by
Barak Norman, London, 1718

An Appalachian Dulcimer from West Virginia, 1875

Two-manual harpsichord, made by Johannes
Dulcker, Antwerp, 1745. Hugo Worch Collection

From the Musical Instruments Collection of the Smithsonian Institution

Smithsonian Institution and Chairman of the Joint Congressional Committee on Construction of a Building for a Museum of History and Technology for the Smithsonian Institution. Dr. Leonard Carmichael, Secretary of the Smithsonian Institution, presided. (He is now Vice-President for Research and Exploration of the National Geographic Society.)

The authorizing legislation for the building established the Joint Congressional Committee for a Museum of History and Technology for the Smithsonian Institution. This Committee has advised the Regents of the Smithsonian on the selection of the design of the building and its construction.

Members of the Joint Congressional Committee since the building project began

Clinton P. Anderson, Senator from New Mexico, Chairman
Wallace Bennett, Senator from Utah
Frank Carlson, Senator from Kansas
J. W. Fulbright, Senator from Arkansas
Edward Martin, Senator from Pennsylvania
Leverett Saltonstall, Senator from Massachusetts
H. Alexander Smith, Senator from New Jersey
Stuart Symington, Senator from Missouri
Frank T. Bow, Representative from Ohio
Overton Brooks, Representative from Louisiana
Clarence Cannon, Representative from Missouri
Laurence Curtis, Representative from Massachusetts
James G. Fulton, Representative from Pennsylvania
Robert E. Jones, Jr., Representative from Alabama
Michael J. Kirwan, Representative from Ohio
John M. Vorys, Representative from Ohio

Members of the Board of Regents since the building project began

Earl Warren, Chancellor

Lyndon B. Johnson	John Nicholas Brown
Richard M. Nixon	William A. M. Burden
Clinton P. Anderson	Vannevar Bush
J. W. Fulbright	Arthur H. Compton
Leverett Saltonstall	Everette Lee DeGolyer
H. Alexander Smith	Robert V. Fleming
Frank T. Bow	Crawford H. Greenewalt
Overton Brooks	Caryl P. Haskins
Clarence Cannon	Jerome C. Hunsaker
Michael J. Kirwan	John M. Vorys

Dr. Leonard Carmichael, as chief administrative officer of the Smithsonian, guided the infant project through its swaddling clothes. Dr. S. Dillon Ripley, who became eighth Secretary on February 1, 1964, is guiding this new project through its adolescence. Mr. James Bradley and Dr. T. Dale Stewart are Assistant Secretary and Acting Assistant Secretary, respectively. Mr. Frank A. Taylor is Director of the United States National Museum and the Museum of History and Technology.

Important as this museum is, it is not intended to overshadow the other working parts of the Smithsonian. For example, the famous Hope diamond is not here but in the gem collection of the National History Building. Each building will continue to have its special purposes, hence in the following chapter is presented the story of the Smithsonian's other "stately mansions."

CHAPTER 7

Early Buildings and Their Uses

Secretary Henry wisely desired that a minimum amount of money be spent on an initial building. He felt that it should be of "plain and durable materials and structure without unnecessary ornament and of sufficient size . . . for the reception and arrangement, upon a liberal scale . . ." of various collections, a library, an art gallery and lecture rooms. Such is the first structure.

The length of the building from East to West is 447 feet and its greatest width is 160 feet. It has nine towers of various shapes ranging from 60 to 145 feet in height.

The architect, James Renwick Jr., was a man of professional distinction. Two other notable buildings designed by him are the Grace Episcopal Church at 10th Street and Broadway, New York City, and St. Patrick's Cathedral. These Churches, of course, are in a quite different style.

This first building was called the Smithsonian Institution. Part of it was ready for occupancy by 1849, and it was virtually completed by 1857. Since it was the only structure, it obviously housed all of the Washington activities of the Institution.

It will be recalled that Henry took only a mild interest in the museum feature, since he conceived the Smithsonian function to be dynamic and worldwide. He wanted no museum to dominate the activities; but his point of view was not shared by Congress.

The act of incorporation of the Smithsonian Institution contained provision for a museum and, to implement this provision, stipulated that "all objects of art and of foreign and curious research, and all objects of natural history, plants, and geological and mineralogical specimens belonging . . . to the United States, which may be in the City of Washington . . . shall be delivered to such persons as may be authorized by the Board of Regents to receive them."

Even had this provision not been made, a museum would have inevitably arisen from the Institution's activities in the increase of knowledge, for such activities, particularly in the fields of anthropology, biology, and geology, entail the collection of specimens and their preservation for scientific study. It was, in fact, the mineralogical cabinet assembled by James Smithson for use in his own researches that formed the beginning of the geology collections.

When Spencer F. Baird came to the Institution as Assistant Secretary in 1850, he brought with him his own large biological collections; and in 1861 the Institution received the very considerable assemblage of specimens brought together by the National Institute—a forerunner of the Smithsonian Institution—which included the noteworthy collections made by the United States Exploring Expedition of 1838 to 1842 under Lieutenant (later Admiral) Charles Wilkes.

The early Government surveys of the new West and the work of the Fish Commission, established in 1871, added greatly to the growing museum, and all these accretions were capped in 1876 by the receipt of many of the American and foreign exhibits of the Philadelphia Centennial Exposition.

Baird was outstandingly a museum man and an activator. He was continually restless, gathering in collections where they might be found. (Not content with his pressing duties, he was a founder of the Cosmos Club in 1878 and was one of its early presidents. It became and still is the outstanding club in Washington for scientists, writers, artists, and professional men of various fields.)

Reconstruction of a Renaissance clock tower. Basic mechanism is that of the town clock of Frederick, Maryland, made by the clock maker Frederick Heisley in 1790.

Duryea Horseless Carriage, built 1893–94. First practical automobile using an internal combustion engine

By the late 1870's it became quite clear that the Smithsonian needed an additional place in which to house the increasing collections. Hence Congress authorized the construction of a new hall to be called the Arts and Industries Building. There was no expense on fancy architecture. The appropriation was two hundred and fifty thousand dollars and General William Tecumseh Sherman was Chairman of the Building Commission. He is the Sherman who marched "from Atlanta to the Sea" breaking the back of the Confederacy. He authored the expression "War is hell." He is perhaps the only public man who refused to be put forward for the presidency. He is reputed to have said that if nominated he would not run, and if elected he would not serve.

Nevertheless, he had both ability and prestige. He began construction of the new hall in April 1879 and completed it in 1881.

For many years, in fact until 1909, the Arts and Industries Building served as the chief museum structure.

The original Smithsonian Institution building became devoted to administration offices, lecture rooms, library space and even lodgings for certain resident and visiting scientists.

Part of the interior was used as storerooms. The manuscripts (many unpublished), souvenirs, and personal effects of James Smithson were stored there and were completely destroyed by fire in 1865. Ironically, most of the building was spared but in that particular section the Smithsonian's most important historic collection was lost.

Later buildings have provided additional space for the growing collections of the Smithsonian, but for thirty years the Arts and Industries Building contained a vast miscellany of exhibits. Here was the initial location of the dresses of the First Ladies of the land beginning with Martha Washington. (These were transferred to the History and Technology Building in 1964.)

Most visitors to the location will recall the airplane *Spirit of St. Louis* in which Lindbergh was the first person to solo across the Atlantic, from the United States to Paris. The original "Kitty Hawk" plane of the Wright Brothers was there and about ten other pioneer airships.

There were numerous industrial exhibits such as early locomotives, early automobiles, and the steel industry exhibit which included the pioneer type of wide-flanged structural beam, also links from the actual chain which during the American Revolution was stretched across the Hudson River from West Point to bar British ships from moving further north.

There were important gifts from individuals, for example the mirror rotor which enabled Michelson to carry on his experiments of measuring the speed of light at the Mt. Wilson Observatory in California. This had been made for Michelson by the Sperry Gyroscope Company, and was presented to the Smithsonian by Preston R. Bassett who became president of Sperry.

Bassett, like various other friends of the Smithsonian, is a repeater. He has donated some half dozen whale-oil lamps, an early surveyor's equipment, and a set of old glassblower's tools, always taking care not to duplicate what the Smithsonian already has.

The annual reports of the secretaries to the Board of Regents list the donors of the year and through the years they aggregate hundreds of individuals. From these sources, from foundations,

Demonstration model of the Figure-8 Stellarator used at the Atoms for Peace Conference in Geneva, Switzerland, 1958

Michelson Rotating Mirror, Division of Physical Sciences, Smithsonian Institution

and of course from explorations, the material of the Smithsonian is constantly growing.

Next in the line of expansion was the National History Building on the right hand side of the Mall as one goes from the Capitol to the Washington Monument. The central unit of the structure was built from 1909 to 1911. The large wings were added much later, under the secretaryship of Leonard Carmichael, and are being used largely for scientific research and for special collections, not open to the general public.

Since the arrangements of the Smithsonian exhibits are inevitably subject to change, certain of the items in this Natural History museum may be moved to other quarters; but this building is so handsome that its contents and purposes are less likely to be subjected to change. The building cost three million five hundred thousand dollars, is of classic design and is finished on all sides in granite. The floor area provides nearly a million square feet.

As mentioned previously, the Hope diamond is exhibited here in the Hall of Gems and Minerals. This was the gift of Harry Winston, New York jeweler, who presented it unobtrusively by mail, sending it to Leonard Carmichael, the seventh secretary, without fanfare.

The history of the Hope Diamond as a symbol of bad luck has been described so often that elaboration seems unnecessary here. One of its early owners was May Yohe, daughter of a storekeeper in Bethlehem, Pennsylvania, who became a musical comedy star of great popularity, but who died in obscurity as a charwoman in Boston, Massachusetts.

The jewel's last individual owner was the late Mrs. Edward B. McLean, who had various misfortunes. Superstitious persons, however, may be cheered by the fact that the evil spell apparently has been exorcised, for Mr. Winston's business had been thriving and the Smithsonian has been prospering even more than ever after being the final owner.

Another piece of jewelry in this collection is the historic diamond necklace that was the gift of Napoleon I to his wife, the Empress Marie-Louise, in 1811, on the occasion of the birth of

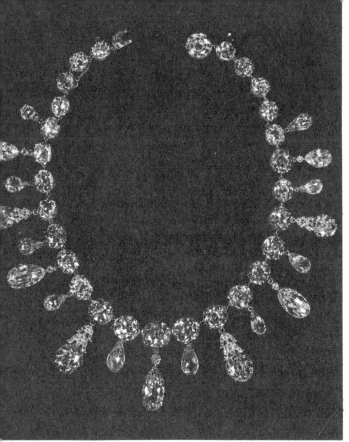

The famous Napoleon necklace

The Hope diamond

their son. This was the gift of Mrs. Marjory Merriweather Post of Washington, D.C., presented in 1962.

The Napoleon necklace was made by Nitot et Fils, the firm in Paris that made most of the other diamond jewelry for Napoleon's use and gifts. This firm was paid 376,274 francs for this gift to the Empress. The necklace is a circle of twenty-eight enormous round diamonds, from which are suspended pendants of briolettes alternating with larger pendants of huge pear-shaped and round diamonds. The total weight of the diamonds is approximately two hundred and seventy-five carats.

After the death of Marie-Louise, in 1847, the necklace passed down through successive generations of her family, the Hapsburgs of Austria. The most recent royal owner of the gems was Prince Franz Joseph II of Lichtenstein, who sold it in 1948.

The Natural History Museum is one of the most rewarding to the nonscientist. Here may be seen a specimen of smithsonite, the ore identified by James Smithson. The specimen here is kelly-green and comes from a mine in New Mexico where the copper content was high, accounting for the color. Smithsonite samples may come in various colors, depending upon what other minerals may be present. The intrinsic composition of smithsonite is a zinc oxide ($ZnCO_3$), as mentioned elsewhere. The specimen may be referred to as a carbonate, as it is here. Another specimen is shown in the carbonate group in the geological exhibit at Princeton University but the O_3 in the composition was the factor that made it a distinct identification by Smithson.

For the industrial scientist in the fields of textiles or paper products, the "Silk Purse" item in the Smithsonian collections is an example of the pioneer breakthroughs in creative chemistry which occurred in the early 1920's.

Arthur D. Little, among other scientists, had been working to develop rayon, cellulose acetate, casein and various synthetic fibers. To attempt to make a silk purse out of a sow's ear was a natural dramatic challenge. This was done. The content of hundreds of boiled-down sow's ears was reduced to a fluid from which could be woven synthetic silk.

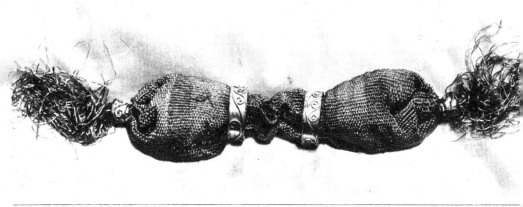

THIS IS THE SILK PURSE MADE OF A SOW'S EAR.

Anyone wishing to see the famous "silk purse," when at the Smithsonian, may see it at the office of the chairman of the Department of Science and Technology.

In addition to these historic items there is on exhibition a fascinating array of ancient musical instruments, many of which have been restored to a playable condition. These include harpsicords, clavichords, and early types of pianos, including horizontal and upright. Besides these percussion instruments there are various specimens in the violin category, hand-plucked strings of the harp and zither type, as well as wind instruments.

However, the largest space of the building is given over to what may be referred to primarily as natural history. Appropriately, the chief exhibit in the building is the huge African bush elephant that stands in the rotunda. It is the gift of J. J. Fénikövi of Madrid, Spain. This is the largest land animal since prehistoric times. It stands thirteen feet at the shoulder, and it weighed twelve tons. Its hide, which weighed two tons, was preserved by the taxidermist and covers an accurately constructed papier-mâché interior.

As distinct from the live animals in the National Zoo, the Natural History exhibits provide dozens of mounted specimens of animals, often displayed against backgrounds of their natural habitats. One may see a considerable assortment of primates, monkeys of many types, including the gorilla.

There are replicas of mountain sheep, white-tailed deer, American elk, mountain goats, and numerous other animals such as bats, giraffes, porpoises and raccoons.

The Bird Hall is elaborate and includes a group of penguins, now stuffed, brought back for the Smithsonian by Admiral Richard E. Byrd from the United States Antarctic Expedition.

There is a large fish collection. Also there are models of early types of human beings similar in character to the exhibits of the Bureau of American Ethnology referred to elsewhere.

The number of items housed in this building runs to the hundreds of thousands. It may be pertinent to refer especially to the specimens in botany totaling several million. It will be recalled that botany was the particular interest of Senator Joel R. Poinsett, an early advocate of the Smithsonian. For him was named the Poinsettia plant. Even as a Frenchman created the word "smithsonite" in honor of Smithson so a Scottish botanist, Robert Graham, added "poinsettia" to the dictionary in honor of the Senator, saying: "I have dedicated it, if not to its original discoverer, at least to one who has first brought it into cultivation and into general notice among botanists, and from whose exertions many additions to our collections of plants from Mexico are expected."

Poinsett had been United States Minister to Mexico and had brought back specimens of that indigenous horticulture, including the plant which became named for him.

The Air Museum

After World War I, a one-story steel structure which had been used for war purposes was turned over to the Smithsonian for the exhibition of aircraft.

In the years which have elapsed it is difficult to think back to the primitive state of aircraft in World War I. The most popular fighting ship was the OX5 which would have been a sitting duck in World War II. By that time it was completely obsolete.

Wright Brothers Aeroplane of 1903

"Spirit of St. Louis"

Diplodocus, giant sauropod dinosaur. Museum of Natural History

African Bush Elephant. Museum of Natural History

Nevertheless, the steel building was all the Smithsonian had available for many years. In it was housed as much memorabilia as it could accommodate. Many aircraft and collateral items have been stored in exterior shelters outside of Washington and will be available when the new Air Museum has been approved and built.

The interim Air Museum has displayed some vitally historic objects, such as the initial space ships. Here are models of the pioneer astronauts with the exact type of airspace clothing which they wore in flight. In front of the building have stood the tall rockets used by the United States in its early exploration of space.

Though the building itself is primitive, the information service of the National Air Museum is up-to-date. Historical, technical, and biographical information on air and space flight is furnished to authors, researchers, historians, schools, Government agencies, and the general public.

The public interest in air and space is tremendous. The visitors

vair's "Atlas" launching vehicle

Original Mercury Spacecraft "Friendship 7" used by John H. Glenn, Jr., on February 20, 1962, for first U.S. earth-orbiting, manned space flight

to this inadequate building in 1962 numbered close to two million. In the following year the total had increased to more than two million six hundred thousand.

The visitors to the Museum and to its related ceremonies have included the late President Kennedy among countless other outstanding citizens of this country, as well as distinguished persons from abroad.

The United States National Museum

The United States National Museum is an administrative title, not a building. Any visitor who might seek to find it in tangible form would be frustrated. For the term refers to the fact that there is a central management over the Museum of Natural History and the Museum of History and Technology.

The full name has been carried intermittently as a recognition of various activities financed primarily by Congress. As early as 1875 a series of publications was begun entitled "Bulletins of the United States National Museum." Furthermore, the full activities of both museums referred to are consolidated into a single bureau for purposes of annual reports. In general, university scientists do not try to keep up with the shifting areas of the Smithsonian but colloquially speak of "The National" just as they would refer to New York (The American Museum of Natural History) or Harvard.

The recent Annual Report of the United States National Museum stated that "catalog entries in all departments now total 57, 541, 770." During that same year, 1,723,850 specimens were added. It is significant that of this total, 1,209,000 were in the Division of Insects.

There is a danger that laymen may be overwhelmed by such staggering statistical presentations. How many of these figures are estimates? Who counts 1,200,000 of insects? Indeed the figure is stated to be 1,209,339. In fact, the reported figures for all the divisions carry out the total to the last digit. For example, in the

Early passenger locomotive, the "Pioneer," built in 1851 for the Cumberland Valley Railroad Co.

Steel Industry Exhibit at the Smithsonian, one of the first industrial presentations.

Division of Reptiles, there was a gift of 325 Colombian frogs. What happens in statistics for the catalog entry if one specimen should disintegrate? There is no intention here to criticize the reports of the various bureau heads who properly report the statistical sizes of their activities, but the Smithsonian receives such an enormous amount of material annually that some simplification of its acceptance procedure and of its cataloging is probable.

A fascinating and unusual addition to the meteorite collection in a single year amounted to twenty specimens. That was a large find, especially as one of these weighed 8.8 kilograms. It fell in the Upper Volta in August 1962, and is being studied in several laboratories because it was of iron composition, which is extremely rare. It will be recalled that James Smithson was passionately interested in the collection and study of meteorites and followed their occurrence in various parts of Europe. It was his exploring for meteorites in Germany which made him a suspect character to the authorities and contributed to his being incarcerated in Hamburg.

CHAPTER 8

Custodian of the Arts

From its inception the Smithsonian has been committed to promotion of the arts.

The act establishing the Institution made a gesture in that direction. Article XIX, Section 5, Subsection 5, called for "a gallery of art."

Secretary Henry, though primarily a scientist, conscientiously attempted to carry out all the provisions of the act. It will be recalled that in the prospectus which he submitted to the colleges and scientific bodies, he mentioned the desirability of providing "a room, free of expense" for the exhibition of objects of art.

In the early decades of the Smithsonian its interest in the arts was negligible; but in 1906 the gift of a valuable collection of paintings willed by the niece of President Buchanan, and the presentation of the Freer Gallery to the Smithsonian made the Institution a leading custodian of the arts. And much has been added over the years.

Other early bequests included a group of paintings by American artists given by William T. Evans, the Ralph Cross Johnson collection of twenty-nine old masters, and the John Gellatly collection of one thousand six hundred and forty art items.

There are so many variables in the jurisdiction of the Smithsonian that it is desirable to note the different divisions relating to the arts under its auspices.

The National Collection of Fine Arts has charge of scores of oil paintings, water colors, and sculptures (aside from those in the Freer and National, or Mellon, Galleries). These are housed in the Natural History Museum and elsewhere, and the collection's distinctive service is providing traveling exhibits for different parts of the United States and abroad. In a single year, for example, 127 shows were circulated to 333 Museums in the United States. The exhibits in the other countries were handled by the United States Information Service. The Smithsonian Art Commission is an advisor on this activity.

The National Portrait Gallery—This is an idea which has been in the process of germination for some time. Ultimately this portrait gallery will be similar in purpose to the National Gallery in London. The old Patent Office Building has been assigned to the Smithsonian to house the Portrait Gallery and the National Collection of Fine Arts mentioned above.

The objective of the National Portrait Gallery acquisition policy is to assure: (1) that likenesses acquired are of persons who have made truly significant contributions to the history, development, and culture of the people of the United States, (2) that appropriate recognition is given to various professions and occupations, and (3) that equitable representation is achieved across the years from colonial times to the present.

The Freer Gallery of Art and the National (Mellon) Gallery of Art will be treated in special sections of this chapter.

The National Cultural Center—This was a special interest of the late John F. Kennedy and is under the jurisdiction of the Smithsonian. Further details are given later in this chapter.

The Freer Gallery—Some of the best representations of Oriental art in the Western Hemisphere are·in the collection of the Freer Gallery of Art of the Smithsonian Institution. Since its opening, in

Note: The Corcoran Gallery, a notable gallery of Washington, D.C., is independently operated and is not a part of the Smithsonian Institution.

1923, the Freer Gallery has come a long way towards the goal of its founder, Charles Lang Freer. In 1906 Mr. Freer gave the Smithsonian his collection of Oriental and American art objects, along with the funds for a building to house the collection. He also gave an endowment fund in trust to the Smithsonian for the study of the civilization of the Orient, as well as for the acquisition of Oriental fine arts. He hoped to set up a center for the study of background cultures as well as the art objects themselves. This endowment has resulted in research lectures, monograph books, occasional papers and catalogs.

The Far East collection includes a wide range of superb examples from China, as well as the arts of Japan, Korea, India, Tibet and Indo-China, the Near East, Iran (Persia), Iraq, Syria, Asia Minor, Byzantium and Egypt.

Included in the collections are the following items from the countries designated:

China: Bronze, jade, sculpture, painting, lacquer, pottery, and porcelain.

Japan: Sculpture, painting, lacquer, pottery, and porcelain.

Korea: Pottery and bronze.

India: Sculpture, manuscripts, and painting.

Iran (Persia): Manuscripts, metalwork, painting, pottery, and sculpture.

Egypt and Syria: Sculpture, manuscripts, glass and metalwork.

In addition, there are Greek, Aramaic, and Armenian Biblical manuscripts, early Christian painting, gold, and crystal.

There are two outstanding objects in this latter group. One is a parchment manuscript of the Gospel, fourth or fifth century. This manuscript once contained the whole of the four gospels, in the order, Matthew, John, Luke, Mark. Some authorities consider it to be definitely fourth century, but the majority leave it at the fourth or fifth.

The second is a rare papyrus manuscript of *The Minor Prophets* (in part). This is third century Greek (Egypt).

A walk through the galleries shows Chinese stone bas-reliefs, bronze religious vessels, Bodhisattvas, many Japanese painted screens, and other objects, all displayed in a most pleasing manner.

Though most of the Museum's galleries contain Oriental objects, the Freer houses a good collection of nineteenth century American art: paintings by Winslow Homer, Albert Pinkham Ryder, John Singer Sargent, Joseph Lindon Smith, George de-Forest Bush, Childe Hassam, Thomas Wilmer Dewing, Gari Melchers, Willard Leroy Metcalf, John Francis Murphy, Charles Adams Platt, Abbott Handerson Thayer, Dwight William Tryon, and John Henry Twachtman; two sculptures by Augustus St. Gaudens, and a group of Pewabic pottery by Mary Chase Perry Stratton. The policy of the foundation prohibits any additions to this section.

The Museum has a large and comprehensive collection of the works of James McNeill Whistler and his "Peacock Room," which is possibly the only remaining example of his work as an interior decorator. It is referred to by some experts as his best decorating effort.

The Peacock Room was created for the display of a collection of blue and white porcelain and is set in a scheme of Oriental grandeur. It was a dining room in the London house of Frederick R. Leyland. Mr. Leyland owned Whistler's portrait, "Rose and Silver, The Princess from the Land of Porcelain," which hangs at one end of the room, and Whistler designed the room around it.

The theme is peacocks and peacock feathers, in gold on blue and blue on gold, interspersed with some green and blue-green. The design was painted in oil colors and gold, on leather, canvas, and wood. At one end of the room, peacocks adorn a large panel, and huge peacocks strut on the shutters. The rest of the decoration was developed from the breast and tail feathers of the bird. The "eyes" of a peacock's tail feathers decorate the ceiling.

Mr. Leyland, who had been away on a trip while Whistler was working, returned to find that Whistler had painted over his favorite and precious Spanish leather in order to decorate the way he wanted to. Mr. Leyland was not satisfied with either this or the design and refused to pay Whistler his price of a thousand guineas. Instead, he gave Whistler one thousand pounds, because Whistler had "wrecked" the room. This was an insult as artists were paid in guineas, each worth a shilling more than a pound. It is said that Whistler asked to be left to finish his decoration, and he painted a caricature of himself and Leyland as the two peacocks on the huge panel facing the "Princess." When Leyland came back into the room he found one peacock whose body was covered with gold coins, with a mass of silver shillings in its claws, the other peacock disdainfully dancing, the background full of floating feathers.

Whistler explained the panel as representing "the rich peacock and the poor peacock," showing the relationship between the artist and his patron.

There are two main floors to the Freer. The upper contains the Peacock Room (Gallery 12), and the Chinese Sculpture Room (Gallery 17), which are permanent exhibitions. Seventeen other galleries surround an open garden court, and the exhibitions in these rooms are changed occasionally. Only a limited number of objects from among the more than ten thousand in the collection are shown in the galleries, but the many other objects in the Museum can be seen by appointment during office hours.

The lower floor of the Museum contains an auditorium, a library, study rooms, laboratories, offices, workshops and storage rooms. There are more than 34,450 books in the library, most of them devoted to subjects represented in the collections. These books are used by staff and students and can be seen during office hours. The Museum has a slide collection of Oriental art. Slides are sold or can be borrowed by institutions or accredited individuals.

The most significant of the additions to the Freer collections between 1953 and 1963 have been in the fields of Ming porcelains and in Japanese painting.

The Freer Gallery continues its studies of the scientific composition of metallic, ceramic, and other objects of art, and the development of new preservation techniques. The Gallery during these years has been a base for the publication, under the auspices of the International Institute for Conservation of Historic and Artistic Works, of the *I.I.C. Abstracts* (commonly called the *Freer Abstracts*). The current number of this journal shows that almost four thousand abstracts of published works on preservation have so far been made available to the whole museum world through this medium.

The Freer Gallery is west of the main building on the grounds of the Smithsonian Institution. It is in the style of Florentine Renaissance palace architecture. Admission to the Gallery is free and it is open every day of the year except Christmas.

As well as being of great aid to scholars, the Freer Gallery of Art is a delight for any casual visitor.

The National Gallery of Art—"The Sacrament of the Last Supper" by Salvador Dali is a striking work. Whether the viewer is among those who think it is a great painting or only a curiosity, it still takes and holds his attention and makes him think. The painting hangs high on a wall as the center of attention in one of the rooms of the National Gallery of Art. The twelve Disciples, heads bowed in reverent attitude, serve to draw the eye to the one face showing, the ethereal, translucent, but strong face of Christ. His sensitivity is remarkably brought forth through Dali's use of paint, and the surrealistic forms tantalize the imagination and draw the mind into fresh channels.

If the visitor is fascinated by the painting he can look through a book on Dali and find that this painting is based on ". . . arithmetical and philosophical cosmogony, founded on the paronoiac sublimity of the number 12, the 12 months of the year, the 12 signs of the Zodiac around the sun, the 12 apostles around the Christ, the 12 pentagons in the celestial dodecahedron, the pentagon containing the microcosmic man, Christ. . . ."* and so on.

Art in its various manifestations undeniably constitutes a

* *Dali, A Study of his Life and Work.* Text by A. Reynolds Morse. New York Graphic Society, Conn., 1958.

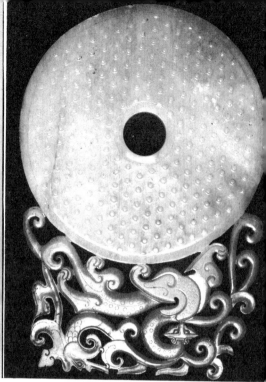

Chinese ceremonial vessel, bronze, Shang
dynasty, ca. 1765–1122 B.C.

Chinese jade carving, Han dynasty,
ca. 200 B.C.

Chinese stone sculpture, scenes from the life of Buddha, 6th century A.D.

Chinese stone sculpture, a Buddhist divinity, 6th century A.D.

Chinese vase, Sung dynasty, 10th century A.D.

Detail of Chinese scroll, 15th century A.D.

Japanese porcelain jar by Kakiemon, 17th century A.D.

Painting by Whistler northeast end of the famous Peacock Room at Freer Gallery, entitled: "The Princess from the Land of Porcelain."

Photographs on these pages courtesy of Freer Gallery of Art, Washington, D.C.

branch of human knowledge—indeed a very important branch as concerns the development of the esthetic, finer side of man's nature. James Smithson placed no restriction on the kinds of knowledge he wanted increased and diffused, and the National Gallery of Art, through its many paintings and its pamphlets, books, and lectures, certainly provokes the imagination and leads to discovery and a wish to learn more.

The National Gallery is one of the most selectively chosen museums in the world. It is a national repository of traditional art formed on the basis of a number of outstanding private collections willed to the nation, such as the Mellon, Kress, Widener, and Chester Dale. It contains European and American painting, sculpture, decorative arts, and graphic arts from the twelfth through the nineteenth centuries, European Old Master paintings, particularly Italian, Dutch, Flemish and Spanish Schools (Mellon, Widener and Kress Collections), French, American and British eighteenth- and nineteenth-century painting, French Impressionist and Post-Impressionist painting (Chester Dale Collection), Garbisch Collection of American Primitive painting, Renaissance, Baroque, and eighteenth-century sculpture, Kress Collection of Renaissance bronzes, Renaissance decorative arts, Chinese porcelains and eighteenth-century French period rooms and decorative arts (Widener Collection), the Rosenwald Collections of prints and drawings, and the Index of American Design. The Gallery is only permitted to show the work of artists who have been dead more than twenty years.

The idea for the museum was born in 1937, when Andrew W. Mellon gave to the United States through the Smithsonian Institution his art collection and a fifteen million dollar gallery building, the whole to be called the National Gallery of Art. (Mr. Mellon was a former Secretary of the Treasury in the United States Government.) This was created as a bureau of the Institution, but the Gallery is largely under the direction of a separate Board of Trustees of which the Secretary of the Smithsonian is an ex-officio member. The United States is pledged to pay the expense of the administration and operation of the Gallery. Begun in June 1937, the building was opened to the public in 1941.

Starting with Mr. Mellon's own collection of one hundred and eleven old masters and twenty-one pieces of sculpture, the National Gallery collection has already grown greater in size and importance through the gifts of several valuable assemblages of art works. As an example of the continuing growth of the Museum, 4,220 works of art were acquired by the Gallery between 1953 and 1963, including outstanding gifts from the Samuel H. Kress Foundation, Horace Havemeyer, William Nelson Cromwell, Syma Busiel, the Fuller Foundation, Incorporated, Mrs. Mellon Bruce, Mrs. P. H. B. Frelinghuysen, and many others.

During this time forty-five temporary loan exhibitions were held and the annual series of lectures delivered (A. W. Mellon Lectures in the Fine Arts).

The earliest paintings in the collection, all of them either Italian or closely related to Italy, are in Galleries 1 and 3. Most of these pictures were done in Florence and Siena, Tuscan cities which were the leading centers of art in the thirteenth and fourteenth centuries. All these paintings are of religious subjects and were intended for the decoration of churches and private chapels. Of particular interest are the "Madonna and Child" by Giotto, and the two panels which originally formed part of Duccio's masterpiece, the "Maesta," in the Siena Cathedral, representing the "Nativity with the Prophets Isaiah and Ezekiel" and "The Calling of the Apostles Peter and Andrew."

Gallery 2 is the first gallery of sculpture. The pieces in it date from the fifteenth century and come chiefly from Florence. Further Renaissance sculpture is displayed in other galleries.

With Gallery 4 the development of Italian painting is carried into its next period. Here the leaders of the early fifteenth century in Florence are represented. Masolino, Fra Angelico, Fra Filippo Lippi, Ghirlandaio, Domenico Veneziano, as well as the Umbro-Florentine Piero della Francesca. Especially to be noticed are two predella panels,* one, the "Healing of Palladia" by Fra Angelico, and the other, "Saint Benedict Orders Saint Maurus to the Rescue of Saint Placidus" by Fra Filippo Lippi. In this gallery are also shown a large "Madonna," and two exquisite predella panels from an altarpiece by Domenico Veneziano, of whose panel paintings little more than a dozen are in existence; a fourth panel by this rare artist, a profile portrait of a man, is in Gallery 7.

In Gallery 5 a parallel development to Florentine painting— which took place in Siena—is shown. Most of the leading artists of the fourteenth century in Siena are represented—Pietro Lorenzetti, Simone Martini and Bartolo di Fredi.

Galleries 7, 8, 9 and 10 contain Florentine, Venetian and Central Italian paintings of the fifteenth and early sixteenth centuries. A new method of painting which appeared in Italy toward the end of the fifteenth century, the use of oil on canvas, is shown here (in addition to the customary use of tempera on panel). To be noted in particular are Botticelli's "Adoration of the Magi" in Gallery 7, and his "Giuliano de' Medici" in Gallery 9.

With Gallery 19 begins a suite of several galleries devoted to early North Italian and Venetian painting. Shown in Gallery 19 are examples of the work of Carlo Crivelli, Mantegna, and outstanding paintings of the Ferrarese School, including the remarkable pair of Bentivoglio portraits by Ercole Roberti, Cossa's "Crucifixion," and "Saint Florian" and "Saint Lucy," originally part of the same altarpiece.

In Galleries 20 and 21 is a noteworthy collection of pictures by the Venetian, Giovanni Bellini. Two famous paintings by Giorgione in Gallery 21, "The Adoration of the Shepherds" and "The Holy Family," introduce the visitor to the Golden Age of Venetian painting.

In Gallery 22 art of the High Renaissance in Venice is displayed. Its greatest exponent, Titian, is represented by two im-

---

* Narrow step or platform at the back of the altar upon which the altarpiece rests, usually a series of small painted panels related in iconography to the altarpiece itself.

portant canvases, a "Venus with a Mirror," and a "Venus and Adonis." In the paintings in this gallery a more pictorial manner of presentation and a more developed oil technique serve to reflect a new opulence and complexity of life. The remarkable "Feast of the Gods" by Bellini (which Titian altered after Bellini's death), shows the beginning of this trend in the early sixteenth century.

In Gallery 23 further examples of Titian's work are shown, together with paintings by Pisanello, Mantegna, Giovanni Bellini, Antonello de Messina, and Boltraffio. Installed in the ceiling of Sculpture Gallery 25 is the only ceiling painting by Titian to be seen outside of Venice. It represents St. John the Evangelist on Patmos and was painted for the Scuola de San Giovanni Evangelista, in Venice.

Of primary importance are the famous "Gritti" and "Farnese" portraits by Titian in Gallery 28, and Tintoretto's "Christ at the Sea of Galilee" and "Conversion of St. Paul" in Gallery 29. In Gallery 30 are hung several paintings by El Greco.

Galleries 35, 35A, 39–43 are devoted to the art of Flanders and Germany. Flemish painting of the fifteenth century, like the work of the early Italian schools, reflects a strong piety. This religious spirit emerges strongly from panels in Gallery 39, such as Jan van Eyck's "The Annunciation," Petrus Christus' "The Nativity," and Hans Memling's "Madonna and Child with Angels."

In Galleries 35 and 35A are further examples of Flemish and German painting of the fifteenth and sixteenth centuries. Most important in Gallery 35A are Grünewald's "Small Crucifixion," the only painting in America by this rare master; Dürer's "Portrait of a Clergyman" and "Madonna and Child"; and Bosch's fantastic "Death and the Miser."

Further on, in Galleries 42 and 43, are examples of the late Flemish painting in the work of Rubens and Van Dyck; the latter is especially well represented by a series of magnificent portraits from his Genoese period.

Dutch painting is seen in Galleries 44–48. Most Dutch painters were interested in recording accurately the details of their sur-

roundings and their everyday life. The supreme expression of realistic effects of light and space is to be found in the work of Jan
Vermeer, who is represented by five paintings in Gallery 44, of
which "A Woman Weighing Gold" is outstanding. These galleries
contain a number of canvases by Frans Hals, as well.

Two entire rooms are devoted to the paintings of Rembrandt
(Galleries 45 and 48). His greatest landscape, "The Mill" is here.
"Lady with an Ostrich-Feather Fan" illustrates the last period of
painting of Rembrandt's life.

In Galleries 49 and 51 are hung examples of seventeenth-cen-
tury Dutch, Flemish, Italian and Spanish painting.

Galleries 52–56 set forth the development of French painting
during the seventeenth and eighteenth centuries, beginning with
figure compositions by Poussin, landscapes with figures by Claude
Lorrain and Louis Le Nain, and an official portrait by Philippe
de Champagne. Connecting the seventeenth and eighteenth centuries is one of Watteau's last great compositions, the "Italian
Comedians." The charming and mundane school of the eighteenth century is represented in several paintings by Fragonard,
notably "A Young Girl Reading," "Blindman's Bluff," and "The
Swing."

Examples of British painting from the time of Reynolds to the
mid-nineteenth century are installed in Galleries 57–59 and 61.
The majority of paintings shown are portraits, and all the leading
portrait painters of the greatest period of British painting are represented here by distinguished examples—Gainsborough, Reynolds, Romney, Raeburn, Hoppner, and Lawrence. Canvases by
Constable and Turner, the outstanding English painters of landscape, are here too.

Gallery 63 is devoted almost entirely to Goya, the greatest Spanish master of the eighteenth and nineteenth centuries.

American painting is shown in Galleries 65–68 and 71. Works
of the early period are mostly devoted to portraiture. American
painting of the later nineteenth and twentieth centuries are exhibited in Galleries 66 and 71. There are several marines by Winslow

Homer, also paintings by Whistler, including the celebrated "White Girl," and an "American Scene" landscape by Inness.

Modern French painting is shown in Galleries 60A, 60B, 62 and 64. This is a loan exhibition of twentieth century paintings of the school of Paris, including works of Modigliani, Picasso, Matisse, Derain, Braque, Dali and others, from the Collection of Mr. Chester Dale. Dali's "The Sacrament of the Last Supper" is among these.

Nineteenth-century French painting is shown in Galleries 72–90, and this includes a few works by related American artists. Among these is a group of canvases by Mary Cassatt. Degas, Renoir, Manet, Corot, Monet, Van Gogh, Gauguin, Toulouse-Lautrec and Henri Rousseau are well represented, as is Cézanne. One of Degas' last paintings, the outstanding "Four Dancers," is here and two rare examples of Renoir's earliest style are in these galleries.

Sculpture in the National Gallery of Art includes a life-size "David" by Donatello which is unique in America. It is in one of the galleries containing the Italian Renaissance sculptures. This collection is not only representative of the major stylistic developments and techniques, it also contains individual items of outstanding quality.

In the Kress Renaissance Bronze Galleries are the famous bronze statuettes, reliefs, plaquettes, medals, and coins formerly known as the Dreyfus Collection of Bronzes, one of the two or three greatest in the world.

French sculpture is represented well. A group of exquisite busts by Houdon, including the "Diana," may be found in Gallery 60.

On the ground floor are galleries where temporary exhibitions are held. There are also a series of exhibition rooms on that floor devoted to the collection of decorative arts, Renaissance furniture, and some superb Flemish tapestries. A room on this floor contains a collection of Renaissance jewelry and medieval goldsmith work. This room contains the twelfth-century "Chalice of Abbot Suger," used by the kings of France for over five hundred years. Other galleries contain Italian Renaissance majolica ware, French enamels of the Renaissance, an extensive collection of late Chinese porcelains ranging from delicate monochrome vessels through vases decorated with elaborate patterns and monumental palace jars and jardinieres. Gallery G-18 contains a paneled room of the Louis XV period in which is exhibited a group of Rembrandt drawings.

The collection of prints and drawings displays selections in Gallery G-19. It contains twenty-two thousand examples from the fifteenth century to the present time. Some of the outstanding specimens are drawings by Campagnola, Schöngauer, Dürer, Hirschvogel, Rembrandt, and Blake. The collection includes one of the most important groups of eighteenth-century French engravings, drawings, and book illustrations outside of France. Most of the great print makers of the Western World are represented by superb impressions, and there is also a fine series of early illuminations. Students may examine prints and drawings not on exhibition, upon request to the curator.

The Index of American Design is a collection of water color renderings of the popular arts in the United States from before 1700 until about 1900. The purpose of the Index was to record designs of historical significance which had not been studied and which stood in danger of being lost; to gather traditional material which might form the basis of an organic development of American design; and to make this material accessible to artists, designers, publishers, museums, libraries, and art schools.

The Index contains color plates of ceramics, furniture, wood carving, glassware, metalwork, tools, utensils, textiles, costumes, etc. Some seventeen thousand finely executed plates and about five thousand photographs may be studied at the National Gallery of Art. The designs are sent out on exhibition and used for study purposes.

The main (second) floor of the museum houses the principal exhibition galleries which are arranged so visitors can follow the development of painting and sculpture as they move from room to room. A central rotunda divides this floor into two wings, each ending in a garden court. The two-story structure provides the greatest amount of natural lighting for the exhibition galleries. This light is filtered through skylights and laylights and is augmented when necessary by artificial lights.

The main exhibition galleries are mostly small in size and decorated with backgrounds suitable for the art of the different periods. In the west wing painted plaster and travertine stone are used in the early Italian rooms, damask in the later Italian, and fumed oak in the Flemish and Dutch rooms. In the east wing, which contains, chiefly, the American, British and French paintings, painted wood paneling is used.

The ground floor is devoted to offices, the cafeteria, smoking room, lecture hall, library, and galleries. These galleries are for the collection of decorative arts, for the supplementary collection of paintings, for prints and drawings, and for temporary or loan exhibitions.

The building faces on the Mall and Constitution Avenue, between 4th and 7th Streets. It was designed by John Russell Pope, Architect, Otto R. Eggers and Daniel P. Higgins, Associates. It is one of the largest marble structures in the world, 785 feet in length, and has more than 500,000 square feet of floor space, with about 238,000 square feet for exhibition purposes.

The exterior is of rose-white Tennessee marble, graded as to shade with the darkest at the base. The suggestion of color counteracts any glare that otherwise might be reflected from the building on bright days. The building is air-conditioned to maintain the proper atmospheric conditions to preserve the Gallery's collections.

The National Gallery has a comprehensive educational program in order to make its collections of greatest value to the public. Gallery tours for visitors twice daily, auditorium lectures and gallery talks, and a fifteen-minute talk on the "Picture of the Week" are given every day. There are free concerts in the Garden Court at eight o'clock each Sunday evening (with the exception of mid-

July through mid-September). The library is open to special students by appointment. Photographs are available there of works of art at the museum, and may be purchased. Many publications of the National Gallery of Art are available at the two Information Rooms, general information booklets, catalogs of paintings and sculpture, color reproductions, and postcards.

Tours and lectures at the museum are given free of charge and slides of objects in the Gallery's collection are available on loan to organizations, schools and colleges without charge. Sets of reproductions with texts, slide-strips, filmstrips, and other material suitable for use in schools are sold in the Information Rooms. Exhibitions of framed reproductions, suitable for schools, colleges and libraries, are available to borrowers for the cost of shipment. Many prepared lectures, using standard Kodachrome slides are also available.

A radio lecture device, running continuously, is installed in exhibition galleries, so arranged that the talks cover most of the periods of art represented by the collection. A visitor may rent a small receiving set for twenty-five cents.

The National Gallery became from the start a center of the study of art in the United States, and is one of the great galleries in the world.

The establishing act provided that the National Cultural Center, now called the Kennedy Center, shall 1) present classical and contemporary music, opera, drama, dance, and poetry, from this and other countries; 2) present lectures and other programs; 3) develop programs for children and youth and the elderly in such arts designed specifically for their participation, education, and recreation; and 4) provide facilities for other civic activities at the Cultural Center.

Congress provided the original site for the structure and authorized the national fund-raising campaign, specifying that funds should be raised by the voluntary contributions of the American people.

The late President Kennedy took the lead in organizing the financial campaign which had several major features. A goal of six million dollars was set to be contributed by American industry. The chairs in the three halls of the Center are to be used for endowments. For one thousand dollars the citizen may have a chair earmarked for him as a founder, and his gift will be acknowledged by a bronze plaque affixed to the back of the seat.

The music of the four United States Military Bands has been recorded for sale to the public. All profits from the sale of the albums are being given to the Center. In one year nearly one hundred and fifty thousand albums were sold.

A campaign was established for the Washington area with the goal of raising seven and a half million dollars. Five thousand workers have been engaged in this effort, which is under the chairmanship of Mrs. Hugh D. Auchincloss, mother of Mrs. Kennedy, widow of the late President.

The building was designed by Edward Durell Stone. It provides a 1,200-seat theatre, 2,750-seat symphony hall, and a 2,500-seat hall for opera, ballet and musicals. In addition, there is a roof garden for band concerts, exhibits, a children's theatre and two restaurants. The design was approved by Mrs. Kennedy, Mrs. Eisenhower, the Board of Trustees and the Commission of Fine Arts.

Rotunda of the National Gallery, showing fountain with Giovanni Bologna's bronze figure of Mercury

"Saint John the Evangelist,"
Umbrian, Master of the
Franciscan Crucifix, 13th
century

National Gallery of Art,
Samuel H. Kress Collection

"David of the Casa
Martelli" by Donatello

National Gallery of Art,
Widener Collection

"Madonna and Child" by Fra Filippo Lippi

National Gallery of Art,
Samuel H. Kress Collection

"Bust of a Lady" by
Desiderio da Settignano

National Gallery of Art,
Samuel H. Kress Collection

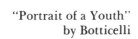

"Portrait of a Youth"
by Botticelli

National Gallery of Art,
Andrew Mellon Collection

"St. George and the Dragon" by Raphael.

National Gallery of Art, *Andrew Mellon Collection*

"Portrait of a Youth" by
Giovanni Antonio Boltraffio

National Gallery of Art,
Ralph and Mary Booth Collection

"A Knight of the Order of
Calatrava" by Miguel Sithium

National Gallery of Art,
Andrew Mellon Collection

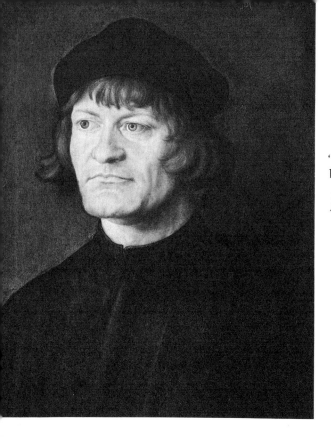

"Portrait of a Clergyman"
by Albrect Dürer

National Gallery of Art,
Kress Collection

"The Needlewoman"
by Velázquez

National Gallery of Art,
Andrew Mellon Collection

"Portait of an Officer" by Frans Hals

National Gallery of Art, *Andrew Mellon Collection*

"The Spinners"
(etching) by Jacques Callot

"The Girl with
a Red Hat"
by Jan Vermeer

"A Woman Holding a Pink"
by Rembrandt

National Gallery of Art,
Andrew Mellon Collection

Playing Card (woodcut),
anonymous Florentine,
17th century

National Gallery of Art,
Rosenwald Collection

"The Maas at Dordrecht" by Aelbert Cuyp

National Gallery of Art, *Andrew Mellon Collection*

"The Singing Party" by William Hogarth

National Gallery of Art, *Gift of Duncan Phillips*

Chinese beaker, porcelain,
K'ang-hsi period, 18th century

National Gallery of Art,
Widener Collection

Chinese Buddhist lion with stand,
K'ang-hsi period, 18th century

National Gallery of Art,
Widener Collection

"Epes Sargent"
by John Singleton Copley

"Venus Consoling Love"
by François Boucher

"Los Caprichos"
(trial proof)
by Francisco Goya

National Gallery of Art,
Rosenwald Collection

"The Skater"
by Gilbert Stuart

National Gallery of Art,
Andrew Mellon Collection

"A View of Salisbury Cathedral" by John Constable

National Gallery of Art, *Andrew Mellon Collection*

"Mortlake Terrace" by Joseph M. W. Turner

National Gallery of Art, *Andrew Mellon Collection*

"John Randolph"
by Gilbert Stuart

National Gallery of Art,
Andrew Mellon Collection

"Lady with a Harp:
Eliza Ridgely"
by Thomas Sully

National Gallery of Art,
Gift of Maude Vetlesen

"Ville D'Avray" by Jean Baptiste Camille Corot

National Gallery of Art, *Gift of Count Cecil Pecci-Blunt*

"Agostina"
by Jean Baptiste Camille Corot

National Gallery of Art,
Chester Dale Collection

"Quadrille at the Moulin Rouge"
by Toulouse-Lautrec

National Gallery of Art,
Chester Dale Collection

"The White Girl" by James A. M. Whistler

National Gallery of Art,
Harris Whittemore Collection

"Madame Monet Under the Willows"
by Claude Monet

National Gallery of Art,
Chester Dale Collection

"A Girl with a Watering Can"
by Auguste Renoir

National Gallery of Art,
Chester Dale Collection

"Repose" by John Singer Sargent

National Gallery of Art, *Gift of Curt H. Reisinger*

"The Church of Saint-Séverin"
by Maurice Utrillo

National Gallery of· Art,
Chester Dale Collection

"The Sacrament of the Last Supper" by Salvador Dali

National Gallery of Art, *Chester Dale Collection*

CHAPTER 9

James Smithson's Final Resting Place

Of all the exhibits in the vast halls of the Smithsonian Institution, the most poignant is that of a tomb, not open to the public but visible in a small room protected by a tall iron grating. Here is the final resting place of the remains of James Smithson, founder of the Institution to which his mind and his money gave birth.

The fact that his remains were brought to America after being buried for seventy-five years in a cemetery in Genoa, Italy, arose from a series of circumstances as unforeseen and unpredictable as many of the events in his life.

As Smithson was a Britisher affiliated with the English Church in Genoa, his body was appropriately buried in the English cemetery in that city. His nephew provided a tomb which bore the inscription, "In token of gratitude to a generous benefactor and as a tribute to departed worth." This tomb was located in a small plot of land surrounded by a fence and was a well-known object of veneration to English visitors. Originally there was no mention there of Smithson being the founder of the famous Institution because, though he had died in 1829, the Smithsonian had not come into being until 1846.

In 1891, however, Samuel P. Langley, the third secretary of the Smithsonian, visited Genoa and caused a memorial plaque to be placed at the graveside, and a similar plaque was placed in the English Church, the Church of the Holy Ghost. From then on, the English colony in Genoa was aware of the interest of the Smithsonian in its famous founder.

The English cemetery was located on a hilltop back of a lagoon in Genoa Harbor and adjacent to the lighthouse. The area was known as the hill of San Benigno. The British had title to the surface of the land but, curiously, not to the earth beneath it. That earth was composed of stone excellent for quarrying. Ultimately, the city coveted that stone to use it in building bulwarks on the shore of the harbor.

It seems the decision to do so, which meant the razing of the hill, proved to be an irremediable engineering mistake, for the hill had been a buffer against winds blowing in from the harbor. It had thus provided a quiet, safe anchorage for vessels using the lagoon. After the hill had been removed, the lagoon was no longer protected and could no longer serve as an anchorage because of its unimpeded high winds. Today the land has been given over to warehouses and other industrial buildings.

By 1900, it had become clear that the continued quarrying would undercut the cemetery land and require the transfer of all the graves in the cemetery to some other location. The authorities were willing to undertake that arduous task, but notified the British that the step was inevitable and imminent. Her Majesty's Consul, in turn, delegated Mr. C. A. Le Mesurier to inform the Smithsonian Institution about the problem. On November 24, 1900, writing from 7 Via Garibaldi, Genoa, he reported to Secretary Langley as follows:

The Committee of the British Burial Ground of Genoa (of which, as you are aware, Her Majesty's consul is chairman), fully realizing how keenly you are interested in all that concerns the resting place of the respected Founder of your Institution, has deputed me to write to you and lay before you the present position of our cemetery.

It will lie in your recollection that when I accompanied you some years ago up to the heights of San Benigno you were struck by the enormous quarry which was slowly but surely eating its way toward us from the sea through the rocky side of the hill on which we stand, and the excavation has lately come so close to us that the intervention of the Consul became necessary to arrest further advance, on the plea that our property would be endangered if the quarrying were carried on.

Actual blasting has in fact been put to an end for the present, and the cemetery (although the boundary wall is now on the very edge of the excavation) remains untouched, but the local authorities who are the owners of the quarry have given us to understand that they need more stone for their harbor works and are therefore anxious to see our graves transferred from the position they now occupy, for which purpose they would give us a suitable piece of ground in another part of the town and would also undertake the due and fitting transport of the remains. Should our answer be in the negative, it is intimated to us that in five years' time, in 1905, the term for applying the law for public utility (twenty years after the date of the last burial) will have been reached, and we shall then have to give up of necessity what we are now asked to yield as a concession.

Under the circumstances the committee have decided that it is their best policy, in the interest of all concerned, to begin to negotiate at once for the transfer on a decorous footing of the British Cemetery and all its tombs, and although some considerable time may elapse before this transfer is accomplished, yet it is evident that the time has now come for us to ask you to prepare your decision as to what is to be done with regard to the James Smithson remains. Are they to be laid with all possible care and reverence in new ground here, or are they to be conveyed to the United States?

The report was laid before a meeting of the Regents, but no immediate action was taken.

The months dragged on, getting continually nearer to the dead-line of 1905, when the remains of James Smithson would have to be transported somewhere. What should be done? Various persons were urging that properly the remains should be brought to America.

A leading spokesman for this view was Gilbert H. Grosvenor,

Editor of the *National Geographic Magazine*. He wrote an eloquent plea for this position in *The New York Herald* of March 1, 1903, which said:

> Dr. S. P. Langley, in a recent sketch of the work of the Institution, of which he is Secretary, states that outside the United States the Institution has more than twelve thousand correspondents scattered through every portion of the globe, and that there is hardly a language or a people where the results of Smithson's benefaction are not known.
>
> The movement that has been started urging that the body of James Smithson be brought to the United States deserves and ought to gain success. If the people to whom he was so generous knew or realized that his remains were about to be disturbed, they would insist on honoring the memory of their great benefactor by bringing them to this country and giving them a permanent resting place in the grounds of the Institution which he founded.
>
> The United States Government ought to assign a warship to carry his body in state across the Atlantic. It would be base ingratitude on our part to let him be buried again in Genoa in another cemetery, where, as time goes on and the city grows, he may be again disturbed. We should place him where he may rest in peace—not for another seventy-five or one hundred years, but for as long as the great nation lives for which he showed such complete confidence and respect.

The United States did not provide a warship as Mr. Grosvenor had suggested, but the Smithsonian did determine to provide the means for bringing the remains to America for a permanent resting place within the Smithsonian grounds.

It commissioned Alexander Graham Bell, the inventor, to carry out this mission. Dr. Bell, with his wife, arrived at Genoa toward the end of December, 1903, and on the morning of December 31, the grave was opened with much ceremony in the presence of William Henry Bishop, Consul of the United States of America; Dr. Bell; Noel Lees, Esq., the official representative of the British Burial Ground Fund Association which held title to the cemetery; Gino Coppede, Genoa architect and engineer charged with opening the tomb; Giovanni Battista Firpo, gardener and custodian for that part of the cemetery where Smithson was buried; Federico Guarini, municipal guard deputed by the city to be present on the occasion; Paolo Parodi, metal worker and chief undertaker, in charge of transferring the remains to a metal casket and soldering the same.

The American Consul formally affirmed when all of this had taken place that the remains consisted of the skeleton which was in perfect condition and that it had been transferred to the casket and placed temporarily in the mortuary chapel of the cemetery, where a guard protected it.

Thus, the remains of the late James Smithson were attended with as much punctilio as if he had been a high official. That would have pleased him. The casket was accompanied to the dock-side by Dr. Bell and the United States Consul at Genoa and placed aboard the steamer *Princess Irene* of the North German Lloyd Line, which sailed for New York on the 7th day of January, 1904.

The ship arrived in New York on the night of January 19th. There, at the direction of President Theodore Roosevelt, the casket was transferred to a government ship and taken to the Navy Yard in Washington, arriving on January 23d.

In the morning of the 25th, the coffin, draped in American and British flags, was borne from the Navy Yard to the Smithsonian accompanied by a troop of the 15th Cavalry, the Marine band, and a detachment of Marines.

The original tomb from Italy was sent for, but was found to be inadequate for an exterior site. A new and beautiful sarcophagus was provided in the style of the original tomb and a small room or chapel was constructed very near the main entrance of the beautiful Norman castle-like building of the Smithsonian. In its present place hundreds of thousands of persons yearly see the founder's tomb, on either side of which appropriately stand the United States and English flags. Surely the dream of Smithson has been fulfilled better than he could have imagined.

REQUIESCAT

CHAPTER 10

"Diffusion" Through Publications

The word "diffusion" in the sense of spreading abroad or communicating, may seem quaint to modern ears, but James Smithson was in good company when he used the word thus. The philosopher Hume in 1752 referred to the "universal diffusion of learning among a people"; and Samuel Johnson in 1750 wrote, "the writer . . . receives little advantage from the diffusion of his name."

From the outset the Smithsonian has paid earnest attention to that part of James Smithson's bequest calling for the diffusion of knowledge, in a variety of ways. Reference has been made to the worldwide exchange of scientific literature known as the International Exchange Service, which has been operated by the Smithsonian for over one hundred and fifteen years. Mention has been made of the Smithsonian Library. There has been brief reference to certain publications. In this chapter, we call attention to the many ways whereby the Smithsonian diffuses knowledge.

Manifold exhibits in the various buildings tell their stories to the many thousands of visitors. As one donor observed, "When on a spring day you see sixty or seventy buses parked outside the Smithsonian—mostly school children—you realize that that is the place to reach the public and do the most good." The same man, himself a scientist and a corporation executive, said "I have visited it regularly several times a year, every year, since 1916."

270

And beyond what is seen by the general public, there is a store-house of knowledge available to the hundreds of scientists who visit the Smithsonian. Workrooms are provided for them where they may see the many specimens brought in from explorations and where they may classify these specimens for the benefit of science. Anyone qualified in a given specialty is welcomed in these inner rooms (there is no desire to exclude anyone), but only an entomologist would be interested in looking at the thousands of beetles that are contained in appropriate cases.

From the early days, the Smithsonian has had a lecture program, and this continues under various auspices. For example, the Freer Gallery has its own program on special art subjects, as do several other branches.

Possibly the most potent form of diffusion is the publication activity of the Smithsonian. The publications past and present may be classified as follows:

1) *Annual Report of the Regents to Congress,* containing yearly a selection of nontechnical articles illustrating recent progress in various branches of science and technology;
2) *Smithsonian Contributions to Knowledge* (terminated in 1914);
3) Smithsonian Miscellaneous Collections, scientific papers on diversified subjects;
4) Smithsonian Special Publications;
5) *Annual Report of the National Museum;*
6) *Bulletin of the National Museum;*
7) *Proceedings of the National Museum,* technical papers on the collections and scientific work of the museum;
8) *Contributions from the National Herbarium;*
9) *Annual Report of the Bureau of American Ethnology;*
10) *Bulletin of the Bureau of American Ethnology,* accounts of research on the customs, languages, and archaeology of the American Indians;
11) publications of the Institute of Social Anthropology (none issued after 1953);

12) *Annals of the Astrophysical Observatory;*

13) *Smithsonian Contributions to Astrophysics,* a series begun in 1956;

14) Catalogs of collections of the National Collection of Fine Arts;

15) Oriental Studies of the Freer Gallery of Art;

16) Freer Gallery of Art *Occasional Papers;*

17) *Ars Orientalis,* a technical series on Eastern Art sponsored jointly by the Smithsonian Institution and the University of Michigan.

The Smithsonian series of tables—physical tables, meteorological tables, geographical tables, and mathematical tables—have long been standard works of reference.

Since its beginning the publications of the institution have been distributed throughout the world, mostly to scientific and literary establishments and libraries; and in return, it has received the publications of like organizations, forming one of the world's largest and most important collections of the serial and monographic publications of scientific, technical, and cultural institutions and societies.

The Smithsonian Library is divided into two principal bodies: the working collections of some half-million volumes, kept for immediate reference at the Institution; and the Smithsonian Deposit of more than a million publications, at the Library of Congress.

The working library is now housed principally in the Natural History Building, but there are a number of decentralized special collections for the use of the various bureaus, departments, and divisions, such as the library of the Bureau of American Ethnology, notably rich in the lore and literature of the American Indians, and the library of the Astrophysical Observatory.

The Smithsonian Deposit in the Library of Congress was initiated in 1866, when Congress passed an act transferring the existing Smithsonian Library to the Library of Congress, where without relinquishing ownership, the Institution might continue to have the use of its volumes as well as those of the Library of Congress. This action was necessitated by the phenomenal growth of the Smithsonian Library during its first twenty years of existence, over-taxing the limited space and funds available for its care.

The Library's primary responsibility is service to the Smithsonian scientific and curatorial staffs, but its resources are available for reference to anyone. Through inter-library loans, it serves research workers and other serious students throughout the country, and by correspondence it answers thousands of reference and bibiliographic questions based on its collections.

These manifold activities, especially in the realm of publications, need a clearing house. While many of the divisions have self-determination for their reports and other publications, who is to help the newcomer seeking information?

The answer is the Editorial and Publications Division, whose chief is Paul H. Oehser.

The Smithsonian Institution, obviously, is a continual source of news, especially in the realm of popular science. Accordingly, the Editorial and Publications Division distributes news releases to a wide list of the press and carries on a large correspondence with those seeking information.

The publications and editorial activities are reported in this book in several places, where pertinent.

For a thorough composite report the reader is referred to bulletin # 13 of the National Science Foundation, Washington, 25, D.C. entitled *Smithsonian Institution*. This is a comprehensive seventeen-page report for sale by the Superintendent of Documents, U.S. Government Printing Office, Washington 25, D.C.—for 15 cents.

CHAPTER 11

The Zoo

The first animals collected by the Smithsonian included six bison which with other animals were kept in sheds behind the original building. The shed animals were increased until there were nearly two hundred, in the original area of the Institution.

The magnificent National Zoological Park in the Rock Creek Valley section of Washington staggers the imagination for the quantity and diversity of its creatures; impressive too are the skill and expertise underlying their treatment.

Tribute must be made here to the pioneer thinking of Secretary Langley. He was not only an airplane designer and an astronomer, but also a devoted student of animal life. He held that the study of animal life was of major importance and essential to an understanding of the world in which man lives. Astutely, he conceived of the idea of keeping live bison on the premises, for the public and Congress were aware that bison had been almost exterminated by hunters and time was short to assure the preservation of the species.

The collection of animals for the purpose of zoological studies was a new concept for the times. It may have been done in remote history for it is known that the Montezumas and the Incas had large collections of animals.

Monarchs from Roman times and earlier had the habit of presenting live creatures as gifts to each other. An emperor in the Middle Ages sent three leopards to Henry III of England in compliment to the fact that this animal appeared in Henry's coat of arms. Another sovereign gave a tawny lioness to George III, having named it Charlotte in honor of His Majesty's consort. Centuries earlier, this type of exchange possibly gave Cleopatra the inspiration for having herself rolled up in a rug and presented to Julius Caesar.

The influence of the presence of the wild bison was enhanced by a report of their custodian, William Temple Hornaday, *The Extermination of the American Bison* which appeared in 1887. It brought national fame to Mr. Hornaday who soon became a zoo director in New York City—a post which he held for many years.

Meanwhile, Hornaday joined enthusiastically with Secretary Langley in evolving the idea of a zoo in which animals could live under conditions which approximated their natural habitats. In Europe the land was so crowded that such a project would have been difficult to achieve in any area near the centers of population; but in Washington the large expanse of Rock Creek Valley was within two or three miles of the Capitol. The wooded and hilly terrain in Rock Creek area, having adequate water supply, was an ideal site for what Langley and Hornaday had in mind.

The Smithsonian at this time regarded seriously not only the care of live animals but also the preservation of knowledge about them through stuffed examples. Hence, the taxidermists looked to the Smithsonian to supply them with specimens. Hence also the various halls of the Smithsonian have created exhibits of stuffed creatures in settings which simulate their natural habitats.

Secretary Langley diligently appealed to the Regents and to Congress to authorize a site for a national zoological park in the Washington area. The Congress authorized such a project in 1889, and in 1890 an act placed the proposed zoological park under the authority of the Smithsonian.

Langley had taken the precaution to provide for a long-range program so that the development would not be of a haphazard

Llamas

Common iguana

Albemarle Island tortoise

Whooper swans

Scarlet king snake

Hippopotamus

nature. Frederick Law Olmsted, a noted architect, was engaged to lay out a long-range plan for the zoo park. The first appropriation by Congress was only two hundred thousand dollars, but at least it was a start.

The new home was made ready for the hundred and eighty-five animals billeted in the Smithsonian sheds. A wagon was borrowed, and in groups ranging from two to several, the creatures were taken on the slow journey from the Mall to Rock Creek Valley until all had been transported.

Attendance of the general public frequently reached ten thousand per day and later the total was nearly thirty thousand. These figures naturally impressed the lawmakers and the District of Columbia, justifying the enterprise as a public benefit.

The problem of creating suitable climate conditions for various foreign creatures proved to be not quite as acute as had been feared. Heat could be provided in winter in certain animal houses; but obviously it was more difficult to provide a cold climate in summertime. Eskimo sled dogs nevertheless had survived satisfactorily in these conditions. Seemingly, kindness, or lack of fear, has had influence on the animals because the amount of breeding in captivity has been exceptional. Black bear, the feline species, antelope, giraffe, and hippopotamus—all of which rarely breed in captivity—have produced young in the Zoo. The herd of bison continued to multiply.

The beaver in this area has ceased to be afraid of man. Normally a wild and shy creature, finding that man here is friendly, he has become tame and will eat out of the hand of the visitor. He is a popular animal because his diligence in building is entertaining to watch, especially for the school children.

It was early discovered that the separation of different species of animals was highly important. For example, if night-roving creatures were billeted close to day-hunting animals the result was insomnia for both types. Most important, of course, is the separation of carnivorous animals from those creatures which are their natural prey in the wilderness.

Soon after the establishment of the National Zoological Park in the early 1890's, a new Congress came into being, and unfortunately it was unfamiliar with the history of the Park. In addition, the panic of 1893 was severe. The Zoo in many quarters was looked upon as nonessential; and it was almost starved out of existence. It was not permitted to buy any animals, and it had to rely solely on gifts, or specimens that it could canvas from the Yellowstone Park.

In time the supply of new animals was greatly augmented by a series of expeditions. The first was that of President Theodore Roosevelt, who went to British East Africa in 1909 to obtain natural history material for the National Museum and to search for animals for the Zoo. Through his efforts, an excellent small collection, including five lions, was obtained. In 1921 and 1922 Dr. W. M. Mann, later Director of the National Zoological Park, accompanied as naturalist the Mulford Biological Exploration of the Amazon Basin, and brought back for the National Zoo a considerable collection, including numerous unusual species.

In 1926 came the first major expedition planned solely for the purpose of collecting live animals for the Zoo—the Smithsonian-Chrysler Expedition to Tanganyika, East Africa. Well-equipped and well-staffed, this enterprise, directed by Dr. Mann, was eminently successful and brought back safely to Washington a large and varied assortment of animals numbering sixteen hundred including giraffes, gnus, antelopes, monkeys, leopards and many other kinds.

The National Geographic Society financed an expedition to collect animals for the National Zoo in the East Indies in 1937, again led by Dr. Mann. This expedition, too, was successful in providing many desirable additions to the Zoo's population, the acquisitions including forty-six species of mammals, ninety-three of birds, and thirty-four of reptiles and amphibians. Localities worked in or represented among the collections were India, Java, Sumatra, the Moluccas, New Guinea and Siam.

Dr. Mann visited Argentina in 1939 for the sole purpose of acquiring for the Zoo a collection of South American animals.

Through the cooperation of zoos, fur farms, and other organizations and individuals in that country he soon assembled a valuable assortment of local mammals and birds to the number of 316 specimens, including guanacos, llamas, capybaras, pampas cats, Brazilian tapirs, and many interesting birds.

Another expedition was made to Liberia, West Africa in 1940, financed by the Firestone & Rubber Co., directed by Dr. Mann. Four separate trips were made into the interior, where animal drives netted many desirable specimens. Altogether, 195 individuals representing 61 species came to the Zoo as a result of this expedition. Among them were chimpanzees, pygmy hippopotamuses, civets, duikers, a potto, a baboon, pythons, cobras, and several kinds of vipers.

In the decade ending in 1963 there were various distinctive additions. One was a fine Bengal tiger from a zoo in India. He is both half-brother and uncle to the Zoo's white tigress. The two animals are now living together and in spite of their complex relationship there is no barrier in the feline world to their producing cubs.

When Ham, the chimpanzee astronaut who soared through space in 1961, was retired in 1963 he was given a place in the Zoo's ape quarters.

Two young polar bears acquired in the Arctic by Washington travelers have been added to the animal colony. The famous Smokey Bear now has a young spouse of the same breed, presented by New Mexico authorities.

The State of Hawaii sent a pair of Hawaiian Geese, a species which had been threatened with extinction by hunters. Though mention has been made here thus far chiefly to animals, the bird collection at the Zoo is substantial, numbering more than 1000. Likewise, the number of reptiles is around 700. There are about 200 creatures living in water, including amphibians, fishes and mollusks. There are also examples of arthropods—animals such as the tarantula with articulated bodies and limbs.

CHAPTER 12

Employment Policies and
Procedure for Giving Objects

There are two subjects which over the years are of particular interest to thousands of friends of the Smithsonian. One is how to inquire about possible employment with the Institution. The other concerns whether certain of a person's possessions might be a desirable addition to the collections of the Smithsonian as a welcome gift.

Employment Policies—The Smithsonian has become such a vast institution that it now employs about 2000 persons in a wide variety of specialized skills, nuclear scientists, trained park police, artists, taxidermists, virtually all branches of manual and cerebral excellence. It needs young people.

The Smithsonian does not promote employment applications, but it is intrinsically in competition with universities and industry who are reaching out for the talented young men and women coming into the field of employment.

Unless the Smithsonian can get its share of the young up-coming geniuses it will have problems for the future.

The 2000 jobs have been filled by the Civil Service where these are on the Government payroll, or by the various bureaus where these are supported by private endowment.

In either case, an applicant should write to the Personnel Office of the Smithsonian, Washington, D.C. The office can give the applicant the appropriate government form if his desire falls within Civil Service, or direct the applicant to the proper bureau.

Various bureaus, science, art, or zoo, undoubtedly will do their own recruiting. That does not mean a closed door. Some jobs of course will be filled by invitation; but any qualified person from any source, or any person who wishes to learn and grow in science or the arts is welcome to apply.

The situation is described by the chief of the Placement Section Personnel Division, as follows:

Programs financed with appropriated funds are staffed from lists of candidates who have qualified in appropriate civil service examinations. Positions covered by such examinations are Museum Curator, Museum Technician, Botanist, Anthropologist, Entomologist, Systematic Zoologist, Geologist, Librarian, Exhibits Specialist, Zoologist, Photographer, Writer-Editor, Animal Keeper, Guard, Astronomers, Physicists, various administrative, secretarial and clerical categories as well as various skilled trades such as Electrician, Carpenter, Plumber, Painter, etc.

Applicants for civil service positions may contact local officers of the U.S. Civil Service Commission, or correspond with the Personnel Division, Smithsonian Institution, concerning specific types of positions. Applications should be forwarded to our office for proper handling.

In recruiting for curators, we generally seek candidates with a Ph.D. in the appropriate subject matter area and appoint at the GS-11/12/13 levels, depending upon experience. Respective salaries at these levels are $8,650, $10,250, $12,075 per annum.

The Smithsonian Institution also administers contracts or grants from other foundations or organizations. Positions in these programs are not under the civil service system and employment is accomplished by the person in charge of the project. The Science Information Exchange, Washington, D.C., and the Astrophysical Observatory, Cambridge, Massachusetts, represent the largest employers in this category, and handle employment through their administrative offices.

Procedure for Giving Objects—Although the collections of the several museums of the Smithsonian Institution are large, they can never be considered complete, because the fields covered are so extensive. The Smithsonian Institution is interested in acquiring significant materials which will fill gaps and round out its collecions.

The subject-matter specialists in the various fields can judge the appropriateness of specimens offered to the Smithsonian Institution for preservation in the national collections. If a person (or institution) possesses an object or collection which may be appropriate for the national collections, and which he wishes to donate to the Smithsonian, he should address a letter describing this material and what he knows of its history to the Registrar, Smithsonian Institution, Washington, D.C. 20560. The Registrar will see that the letter is directed to the appropriate subject-matter specialist for consideration.

The Smithsonian is most appreciative of any offers of objects or other expressions of interest in its scientific and museum programs.

UNITED STATES CIVIL SERVICE COMMISSION
WASHINGTON, D.C. 20415

A GENERAL AMENDMENT

showing the new salary rates for positions in the Federal Government under the General Schedule in accordance with the Federal Employees Salary Act of 1964.

This amendment applies to all civil service examination announcements currently open for receipt of applications except those specifically amended to provide for higher minimum pay rates.

TABLE SHOWING CURRENT SALARY RATES FOR THE GENERAL SCHEDULE

Grade	Current Basic Salary	Current Maximum Salary
GS–1	$ 3,385	$ 4,420
GS–2	3,680	4,805
GS–3	4,005	5,220
GS–4	4,480	5,830
GS–5	5,000	6,485
GS–6	5,505	7,170
GS–7	6,050	7,850
GS–8	6,630	8,610
GS–9	7,220	9,425
GS–10	7,900	10,330
GS–11	8,650	11,305
GS–12	10,250	13,445
GS–13	12,075	15,855
GS–14	14,170	18,580
GS–15	16,460	21,590

Employees who perform at an acceptable level of competence will receive periodic within-grade increases beyond the basic salary until the maximum rate for the grade is reached.

This amendment supersedes the previous General Amendment concerning salary rates dated January 1964.

ISSUED: August 1964

Appendix

Officers, Committees and Staff of the Smithsonian Institution as of 1965

Presiding Officer ex officio.—LYNDON B. JOHNSON, President of the United States.

Chancellor.—EARL WARREN, Chief Justice of the United States.

Members of the Institution:

    LYNDON B. JOHNSON, President of the United States.

    HUBERT H. HUMPHREY, Vice President of the United States.

    EARL WARREN, Chief Justice of the United States.

    DEAN RUSK, Secretary of State.

    *DOUGLAS DILLON, Secretary of the Treasury.

    ROBERT S. MCNAMARA, Secretary of Defense.

    *ROBERT F. KENNEDY, Attorney General.

    JOHN A. GRONOUSKI, Postmaster General.

    STEWART L. UDALL, Secretary of the Interior.

    ORVILLE L. FREEMAN, Secretary of Agriculture.

    *LUTHER H. HODGES, Secretary of Commerce.

    W. WILLARD WIRTZ, Secretary of Labor.

    ANTHONY J. CELEBREZZE, Secretary of Health, Education and Welfare.

* replaced in 1965.

Regents of the Institution:

EARL WARREN, Chief Justice of the United States, Chancellor.

HUBERT H. HUMPHREY, Vice President of the United States.

CLINTON P. ANDERSON, Member of the Senate.

J. WILLIAM FULBRIGHT, Member of the Senate.

LEVERETT SALTONSTALL, Member of the Senate.

FRANK T. BOW, Member of the House of Representatives.

MICHAEL J. KIRWAN, Member of the House of Representatives.

GEORGE H. MAHON, Member of the House of Representatives.

JOHN NICHOLAS BROWN, citizen of Rhode Island.

WILLIAM A. M. BURDEN, citizen of New York.

ROBERT V. FLEMING, citizen of Washington, D.C.

CRAWFORD H. GREENEWALT, citizen of Delaware.

CARYL P. HASKINS, citizen of Washington, D.C.

JEROME C. HUNSAKER, citizen of Massachusetts.

Executive Committee.—ROBERT V. FLEMING, *Chairman;* CARYL P. HASKINS, CLINTON P. ANDERSON.

Secretary.— S. DILLON RIPLEY.

Assistant Secretary.—JAMES C. BRADLEY.

Acting Assistant Secretary.—T. D. STEWART.

Assistant to the Secretary.—THEODORE W. TAYLOR.

Special Assistants to the Secretary:

For Fine Arts, THOMAS M. BEGGS;

For Traveling Exhibition Study, MRS. ANNEMARIE POPE;

For Scientific Matters, PHILIP C. RITTERBUSH.

Consultant to the Secretary for International Activities.—WILLIAM WARNER.

Administrative Assistant to the Secretary.—MRS. LOUISE M. PEARSON.

Treasurer.—EDGAR L. ROY.

Chief, Editorial and Publications Division.—PAUL H. OEHSER.

Librarian.—RUTH E. BLANCHARD.

Curator, Smithsonian Museum Service.—G. CARROLL LINDSAY.

Buildings Manager.—ANDREW F. MICHAELS, JR.

Director of Personnel.—J. A. KENNEDY.

Chief, Supply Division.—A. W. WILDING.

Chief, Photographic Service Division.—O. H. GREESON.

UNITED STATES NATIONAL MUSEUM

Director.—F. A. Taylor.

Registrar.—Helena M. Weiss.

MUSEUM OF NATURAL HISTORY

Director.—T. D. Stewart.

Assistant Directors.—R. S. Cowan, I. E. Wallen.

Administrative Officer.—Mrs. Mabel A. Byrd.

DEPARTMENT OF ANTHROPOLOGY: W. R. Wedel, chairman; A. J. Andrews, exhibits specialist.

> *Division of Archaeology:* Clifford Evans, Jr., R. B. Woodbury, curators; G. W. Van Beek, associate curator.

> *Division of Ethnology:* S. H. Riesenberg, curator; G. D. Gibson, E. I. Knez, W. H. Crocker, associate curators.

> *Division of Physical Anthropology:* J. L. Angel, curator; Lucile E. Hoyme, associate curator.

DEPARTMENT OF ZOOLOGY: H. H. Hobbs, Jr., chairman; F. A. Chace, Jr., senior scientist; W. M. Perrygo, in charge of taxidermy.

> *Division of Mammals:* D. H. Johnson, curator; H. W. Setzer, C. O. Handley, Jr., associate curators.

> *Division of Birds:* P. S. Humphrey, curator; G. E. Watson, R. I. Zusi, associate curators.

> *Division of Reptiles and Amphibians:* Doris M. Cochran, curator.

> *Division of Fishes:* L. P. Schultz, curator; E. A. Lachner, W. R. Taylor, V. G. Springer, S. H. Weitzman, R. H. Gibbs, Jr., associate curators.

> *Division of Marine Invertebrates:* D. F. Squires, curator; T. E. Bowman, C. E. Cutress, Jr., Marian H. Pettibone, R. B. Manning, D. L. Pawson, associate curators.

> *Division of Mollusks:* H. A. Rehder, curator; J. P. E. Morrison, Joseph Rosewater, associate curators.

DEPARTMENT OF ENTOMOLOGY: J. F. G. Clarke, chairman.

> *Division of Neuropteroids:* O. S. Flint, Jr., associate curator in charge.

> *Division of Lepidoptera:* J. F. G. Clarke, acting curator; D. R. Davis, W. D. Duckworth, W. D. Field, associate curators.

Division of Coleoptera: O. L. Cartwright, curator; P. J. Spangler, associate curator.

Division of Hemiptera: R. C. Froeschner, associate curator in charge.

Division of Myriapoda and Arachnida: R. E. Crabill, Jr., curator.

DEPARTMENT OF BOTANY (NATIONAL HERBARIUM): J. R. Swallen, chairman.

Division of Phanerogams: L. B. Smith, curator; Velva E. Rudd, J. J. Wurdack, W. R. Ernst, D. H. Nicolson, S. G. Shetler, associate curators.

Division of Ferns: C. V. Morton, curator; D. B. Lellinger, associate curator.

Division of Grasses: J. R. Swallen, acting curator; T. R. Soderstrom, associate curator.

Division of Cryptogams: M. E. Hale, Jr., curator; P. S. Conger, H. E. Robinson, associate curators.

Division of Plant Anatomy: W. L. Stern, curator; R. H. Eyde, associate curator.

DEPARTMENT OF PALEOBIOLOGY: G. A. Cooper, chairman.

Division of Invertebrate Paleontology: R. S. Boardman, curator; P. M. Kier, Richard Cifelli, E. G. Kauffman, M. A. Buzas, R. H. Benson, associate curators.

Division of Vertebrate Paleontology: C. L. Gazin, curator; D. H. Dunkle, Nicholas Hotton III, C. E. Ray, associate curators.

Division of Paleobotany: F. M. Hueber, curator; W. H. Adey, associate curator.

DEPARTMENT OF MINERAL SCIENCES: G. S. Switzer, chairman.

Division of Mineralogy: G. S. Switzer, acting curator; P. E. Desautels, associate curator.

Division of Meteorites: E. P. Henderson, associate curator in charge; R. S. Clarke, Jr., chemist.

OCEANOGRAPHY PROGRAM: I. E. Wallen, assistant director; H. A. Fehlmann, supervisory museum specialist, Smithsonian Oceanographic Sorting Center.

MUSEUM OF HISTORY AND TECHNOLOGY

Director.—F. A. Taylor.

Assistant Director.—J. C. Ewers.

Administration officers.—W. E. Boyle, Virginia Beets.

DEPARTMENT OF SCIENCE AND TECHNOLOGY: R. P. Multhauf, chairman; Deborah J. Mills, assistant curator.

Division of Physical Sciences: R. P. Multhauf, curator; W. F. Cannon, Uta C. Merzbach, associate curators.

Division of Mechanical and Civil Engineering: S. A. Bedini, curator; E. A. Battison, R. M. Vogel, associate curators.

Division of Transportation: H. I. Chapelle, curator; K. M. Perry, J. H. White, Jr., associate curators.

Division of Electricity: B. S. Finn, associate curator in charge.

Division of Medical Sciences: S. K. Hamarneh, curator.

DEPARTMENT OF ARTS AND MANUFACTURERS: P. W. Bishop, chairman.

Division of Textiles: Mrs. Grace R. Cooper, curator; Rita J. Adrosko, associate curator.

Division of Ceramics and Glass: P. V. Gardner, curator; J. J. Miller II, associate curator.

Division of Graphic Arts: Jacob Kainen, curator; F. O. Griffith, Eugene Ostroff, associate curators.

Division of Manufactures and Heavy Industries: P. W. Bishop, acting curator; L. L. Hinkle, industrial specialist.

Division of Agriculture and Forest Products: E. C. Kendall, associate curator in charge.

DEPARTMENT OF CIVIL HISTORY: R. H. Howland, chairman; P. C. Welsh, curator; Mrs. Doris E. Borthwick, Anne Castrodale, assistant curators.

Division of Political History: W. E. Washburn, curator; Mrs. Margaret Brown Klapthor, K. E. Melder, Mrs. Anne W. Murray, associate curators; H. R. Collins, assistant curator.

Division of Cultural History: C. M. Watkins, curator; Mrs. Cynthia A. Hoover, J. N. Pearce, Rodris C. Roth, associate curators.

Division of Philately and Postal History: C. H. Scheele, associate curator in charge.

Division of Numismatics: Vladimir Clain-Stefanelli, curator; Mrs. Elvira Clain-Stefanelli, associate curator.

DEPARTMENT OF ARMED FORCES HISTORY: M. L. Peterson, chairman.

Division of Military History: E. M. Howell, curator; C. R. Goins, Jr., associate curator.

Division of Naval History: P. K. Lundeberg, curator; M. H. Jackson, associate curator.

OFFICE OF EXHIBITS

Chief.—J. E. Anglim.
Museum of Natural History Laboratory: A. G. Wright, assistant chief; Julius Tretick, production supervisor.
Museum of History and Technology Laboratory: B. W. Lawless, chief.

CONSERVATION RESEARCH LABORATORY

Conservator-in-charge.—C. H. Olin.
Chemist.—Mrs. Jacqueline S. Olin.

INTERNATIONAL EXCHANGE SERVICE

Chief.—J. A. Collins.

NATIONAL ZOOLOGICAL PARK

Director.—T. H. Reed.
Associate Director.—J. L. Grimmer.
Administrative Assistant.—Travis E. Fauntleroy.
Zoologist.—Marion McCrane.
Veterinarian.—Clinton W. Gray.

BUREAU OF AMERICAN ETHNOLOGY

Acting Director.—Henry B. Collins.
Anthropologists.—H. B. Collins, R. L. Stephenson, W. C. Sturtevant, Robert M. Laughlin.
RIVER BASIN SURVEYS.—R. L. Stephenson, *Acting Director.*

ASTROPHYSICAL OBSERVATORY

Director.—F. L. Whipple.
Assistant Directors.—C. W. Tillinghast, Charles Lundquist.
Astronomers.—G. Colombo, L. Goldberg, G. S. Hawkins, I. G. Izsak, Y. Kozai, R. Martin, J. Slowey, L. Solomon, F. W. Wright.
Mathematicians.—R. W. Briggs, D. A. Lautman.
Physicists.—E. Avrett, N. P. Carleton, A. F. Cook, R. J. Davis, J. DeFelice, C. H. Dugan, G. G. Fazio, E. L. Fireman, F. Franklin, O. Gin-

gerich, M. Grossi, P. V. Hodge, W. M. Irvine, L. G. Jacchia, W. Kalkofen, R. E. McCrosky, H. Mitler, R. W. Noyes, C. E. Sagan, A. Skalafuris, R. B. Southworth, D. Tilles, C. A. Whitney.

Geodesists.—W. Köhnlein, J. Rolff, G. Veis.

Geologists.—O. B. Marvin, J. Wood.

DIVISION OF RADIATION AND ORGANISMS:

Chief.—W. H. Klein.

Assistant Chief.—W. Shropshire.

Biochemists.—D. L. Correll, M. M. Margulies.

Geochemists.—A. Long.

Plant physiologists.—J. L. Edwards, V. B. Elstad, L. Loercher, K. Mitrakos, L. Price, A. M. Steiner.

Electronic engineers.—J. H. Harrison, H. J. Lehfeldt.

Instrument engineering technicians.—D. G. Talbert, W. N. Cogswell.

Physicist.—B. Goldberg.

NATIONAL COLLECTION OF FINE ARTS

Acting Director.—David W. Scott.

Associate Curator.—Rowland Lyon.

SMITHSONIAN INSTITUTION TRAVELING EXHIBITION SERVICE.—Mrs. Dorothy Van Arsdale, *Acting Chief.*

SMITHSONIAN ART COMMISSION.—Paul Manship (chairman), S. Dillon Ripley (secretary), Gilmore D. Clarke, (vice chairman), Page Cross, David E. Finley, Lloyd Goodrich, Walker Hancock, Bartlett H. Hayes, Jr., Wilmarth S. Lewis, Henry P. McIlhenny, Paul Mellon, Ogden M. Pleissner, Edgar P. Richardson, Charles H. Sawyer, Stow Wengenroth, Andrew Wyeth; Alexander Wetmore, Leonard Carmichael (members emeritus).

FREER GALLERY OF ART

Director.—John A. Pope.

Assistant Director.—Harold P. Stern.

Head Curator, Near Eastern Art.—Richard Ettinghausen.

Associate Curator, Chinese Art.—James F. Cahill.

Head Curator, Laboratory.—Rutherford J. Gettens.

NATIONAL GALLERY OF ART

Trustees:
  EARL WARREN, Chief Justice of the United States, *Chairman.*
  DEAN RUSK, Secretary of State.
  DOUGLAS DILLON, Secretary of the Treasury.
  S. DILLON RIPLEY, Secretary of the Smithsonian Institution.
  JOHN N. IRWIN II.
  PAUL MELLON.
  FRANKLIN D. MURPHY.
  LESSING J. ROSENWALD.
  JOHN HAY WHITNEY.
*President.—*PAUL MELLON.
*Vice President.—*JOHN HAY WHITNEY.
*Secretary-Treasurer.—*HUNTINGTON CAIRNS.
*Director.—*JOHN WALKER.
*Administrator.—*ERNEST R. FEIDLER.
*General Counsel.—*HUNTINGTON CAIRNS.
*Chief Curator.—*PERRY B. COTT.
*Assistant Director.—*J. CARTER BROWN.

NATIONAL AIR MUSEUM

Advisory Board:
  S. Dillon Ripley, *Chairman.*
  Maj. Gen. Brooke E. Allen, U.S. Air Force.
  Vice Adm. William A. Schoech, U.S. Navy.
  James H. Doolittle (Lt. Gen., U.S.A.F. Ret.)
  Grover Loening.
*Director.—*P. S. Hopkins.
*Head Curator and Historian.—*P. E. Garber.
*Curators.—*L. S. Casey, R. B. Meyer, K. E. Newland.

CANAL ZONE BIOLOGICAL AREA

*Director.—*M. H. Moynihan.
*Biologists.—*Robert L. Dressler, Neal G. Smith.

JOHN F. KENNEDY CENTER FOR THE PERFORMING ARTS

Trustees:
  HOWARD F. AHMANSON.
  FLOYD D. AKERS.

Lucius D. Battle, Assistant Secretary of State for Educational and Cultural Affairs, *ex officio.*

Ralph E. Becker.

K. Le Moyne Billings.

Ernest R. Breech.

Edgar M. Bronfman.

Ralph J. Bunche.

Anthony J. Celebrezze, Secretary of Health, Education, and Welfare, *ex officio.*

Joseph S. Clark.

J. William Fulbright.

Mrs. George A. Garrett.

George B. Hartzog, Director of the National Park Service, *ex officio.*

Francis Keppel, Commissioner, U.S. Office of Education, *ex officio.*

Mrs. Albert D. Lasker.

George Meany.

L. Quincy Mumford, Librarian of Congress, *ex officio.*

Mrs. Charlotte T. Reid.

Richard S. Reynolds, Jr.

Frank H. Ricketson, Jr.

S. Dillon Ripley, Secretary of the Smithsonian Institution, *ex officio.*

Leverett Saltonstall.

Mrs. Jouett Shouse.

Roger L. Stevens.

L. Corrin Strong.

Frank Thompson.

Walter N. Tobriner, President D.C. Board of Commissioners, *ex officio.*

William Walton, Chairman, Commission of Fine Arts, *ex officio.*

William M. Waters, Jr., Chairman, D.C. Recreation Board, *ex officio.*

Jim Wright.

Officers:

Honorary Chairmen.—Mrs. Dwight D. Eisenhower, Mrs. Lyndon B. Johnson, Mrs. John F. Kennedy.

Chairman.—Roger L. Stevens.

Vice chairman.—L. CORRIN STRONG.

Treasurer.—DANIEL W. BELL.

Counsel.—RALPH E. BECKER.

Secretary.—K. LE MOYNE BILLINGS.

Senior Assistant Secretary.—PHILIP J. MULLIN.

Chairman, Advisory Committee on the Arts.—ROBERT W. DOWLING.

NATIONAL PORTRAIT GALLERY

National Portrait Gallery Commission:

CATHERINE DRINKER BOWEN.

JULIAN P. BOYD.

JOHN NICHOLAS BROWN, *Chairman.*

LEWIS DESCHLER.

DAVID E. FINLEY.

WILMARTH SHELDON LEWIS.

S. DILLON RIPLEY, Secretary of the Smithsonian Institution, *ex officio.*

RICHARD H. SHRYOCK.

FREDERICK P. TODD.

JOHN WALKER, Director of the National Gallery of Art, *ex officio.*

EARL WARREN, Chief Justice of the United States, *ex officio.*

NATIONAL ARMED FORCES MUSEUM ADVISORY BOARD

STEPHEN AILES, Secretary of the Army.

JOHN NICHOLAS BROWN, *Chairman.*

MRS. JEAN KINTNER.

DAVID LLOYD KREEGER.

ROBERT S. McNAMARA, Secretary of Defense, *ex officio.*

PAUL H. NITZE, Secretary of the Navy.

WILLIAM H. PERKINS, JR.

S. DILLON RIPLEY, Secretary of the Smithsonian Institution, *ex officio.*

EARL WARREN, Chief Justice of the United States; Chancellor of the Smithsonian Institution.

HENRY BRADFORD WASHBURN, JR.

EUGENE M. ZUCKERT, Secretary of the Air Force.

Honorary Smithsonian Fellows, Collaborators, Associates, Custodians of Collections, and Honorary Curators

OFFICE OF THE SECRETARY

John E. Graf

UNITED STATES NATIONAL MUSEUM

MUSEUM OF NATURAL HISTORY

Anthropology

J. M. Campbell, Archaeology.
C. G. Holland, Archaeology.
N. M. Judd, Archaeology.
Betty J. Meggers, Archaeology.
F. M. Setzler, Anthropology.

W. W. Taylor, Jr., Anthropology.
W. J. Tobin, Physical Anthropology.
Nathalie F. S. Woodbury, Archaeology.

Zoology

O. L. Austin, Birds.
W. W. Becklund, Helminthology.
J. Bruce Bredin, Biology.
W. L. Brown, Mammals.
Leonard Carmichael, Psychology and Animal Behavior.
Ailsa M. Clark, Marine Invertebrates.
H. G. Deignan, Birds.
Robert W. Fricken, Birds.
Herbert Friedmann, Birds.
Laurence Irving, Birds.

Allen McIntosh, Mollusks.
J. P. Moore, Marine Invertebrates.
Dioscoro S. Rabor, Birds.
W. L. Schmitt, Marine Invertebrates.
Benjamin Schwartz, Helminthology.
Robert Traub, Mammals.
Alexander Wetmore, Birds.
Mrs. Mildred S. Wilson, Copepod Crustacea.

Entomology

Doris H. Blake.
M. A. Carriker, Jr.
C. J. Drake.
K. C. Emerson.

F. M. Hull.
W. L. Jellison.
C. F. W. Muesebeck.
T. E. Snyder.

Botany

C. R. Benjamin, Fungi.
E. C. Leonard, Phanerogams.
F. A. McClure, Grasses.

Mrs. Kittie F. Parker, Phanerogams.
J. A. Stevenson, Fungi.
W. N. Watkins, Woods.

Paleobiology

C. W. Cooke, Invertebrate Paleontology.
J. T. Dutro, Invertebrate Paleontology.
Remington Kellogg, Vertebrate Paleontology.

A. A. Olsson, Invertebrate Paleontology.
W. P. Woodring, Invertebrate Paleontology.

Mineral Sciences

Gunnar Kullerud, Mineralogy.

W. T. Schaller, Mineralogy.

MUSEUM OF HISTORY AND TECHNOLOGY

Science and Technology

D. J. Price

Civil History

Mrs. Arthur M. Greenwood, Cultural History.
E. C. Herber, History.
I. N. Hume, Cultural History.
F. W. McKay, Numismatics.

Mrs. R. Henry Norweb, Numismatics.
R. Henry Norweb, Numismatics.
Joan Jockwig Pearson, Cultural History.

Armed Forces History

W. R. Furlong.
F. C. Lane.

Bryon McCandless.

Exhibits

W. L. Brown, Taxidermy

BUREAU OF AMERICAN ETHNOLOGY

Sister M. Inez Hilger.
Frank H. H. Roberts.

M. W. Stirling.
A. J. Waring, Jr.

Astrophysical Observatory

C. G. Abbot

Freer Gallery of Art

Oleg Grabar.

Grace Dunham Guest.

Max Loehr.

Katherine N. Rhoades.

National Air Museum

Frederick C. Crawford.

Alfred V. Verille.

National Zoological Park

E. P. Walker

Canal Zone Biological Area

C. C. Soper

Acknowledgments

The manifold sources essential to the presentation of this book obviously have compassed both Europe and America. It is possible here to mention only a few institutions and individuals who have been closely identified with this work. For convenience we do this geographically.

Washington, D.C.

Obviously many of the Smithsonian Institution staff participated through their works or in person in this report. Paul H. Oehser, Chief, Educational and Publications Division, was the major contining contact with the authors.

A general acknowledgment of the Smithsonian's aid and sources is contained in the phrase on our title page which reads "with the Smithsonian." The use of this phrase was authorized by the Institution.

G. R. Wright of Silver Spring, Maryland, deserves special mention for his knowledge and his equipment in a Moonwatch station. Mr. Wright has an unusual array of telescopes, from simple hand devices usable by the merest amateur, to high-power instruments.

England

Miss Mavis Mackinnon was the continuing researcher for this project in England over a period of many months. Her name originally was suggested by the British Museum. She delved there, at the Public Record Office, Somerset House, the Royal Society, the Royal Institution, and other standard sources. At the direction of the authors she also investigated correspondence collections of the era and obtained the cooperation of the Hoare Bank, the Drummond Bank, and the Bank of England, who made available the financial records of James Smithson and his mother, Mrs. Macie. Miss Mackinnon also contributed original research, such as discovering the marriage record of Mrs. Macie at St. Paul's Cathedral, London. (Previously it had been assumed that she was married at Bath, and the absence of any record there had been a mystery.)

Historical Society of Bath. Diligent search was made by this society in collaboration with author Long. Only meager records remain of husband John Macie. The chief record is a tablet to his memory in the Cathedral Church.

R. B. McCallum, Master, Pembroke College, Oxford University, provided important, hitherto unpublished, original documents. These included the weekly board bills of Smithson (then known as Macie) and his classmates, his entrance application to Oxford, and his record of attendance and absences (evidenced by the dating of the board bills). Master McCallum also unearthed illustrations of Pembroke College and St. Aldate's Church as they appeared in Smithson's time.

The Verger of Westminster Abbey provided a copy of the Register of the Abbey, as well as verbal comments on the history of the first Duke of Northumberland and those of his family who are buried in the Abbey. Smithson, his illegitimate son did not have that privilege, but two illegitimate daughters are buried there.

Europe

Smithson traveled extensively in Germany, Denmark, and elsewhere on the Continent. He lived for various long periods in France. He lived in Florence, also, and in Genoa before his death. Most of our knowledge of him in these areas comes from his own correspondence, preserved in widely scattered areas, some in Florence, some in Philadelphia, some in San Francisco. The absence of records may be accounted for in part by the looting by the Germans in 1870, World War I, and World War II, when they removed tons of records from Paris, including vital statistics and property deeds.

Mrs. Geoffrey Parsons of Paris made a search of the history of 121 Montmartre where Smithson lived (his visiting card is extant). In 1963, author Long saw the handsome structure, then in an industrial neighborhood. By 1964 it was in the process of being torn down.

Stephen P. Dorsey, American Consul General in Genoa (now stationed in Rome, supervising all the American consulates in Italy) was most helpful in indicating the last evidences of Smithson's life in Genoa, where he died. The English church which Smithson attended still stands, and there are various records of his existence.

Signorina Argentina Sacchi-Nemours, recommended by Mr. Dorsey, acted as interpreter and researcher. Smithson's Genoa banker is known; the location of Smithson's burial place (until his remains were moved to Washington) is certain. The official consular records of his death and properties—even to his laundry —are established.

The removal of the Smithson remains to the United States is all part of the Smithsonian record and is described in Part III, Chapter 9.

Princeton, New Jersey

So many Princeton sources have commented on the preparation of the manuscript that it is difficult to single out individual names.

Various individual university faculty members have been consulted, such as Sir Hugh Taylor, but the text is the sole responsibility of the authors.

William S. Dix, Librarian, and A. P. Clark, Rare Books and Manuscripts, of the Princeton University Library, should be especially mentioned for referring to important source material.

Two researchers assisting author Long over a two-year period are:

Sally-Lou Bailey (Mrs. William Bailey) who tracked down numerous leads and made useful suggestions.

E. Joan Horrocks (Mrs. William Horrocks), formerly on the staff of the Metropolitan Museum of Art, New York. Mrs. Horrocks was especially useful in reviewing the art activities of the Smithsonian. Guided by the official pamphlets of the respective galleries, she wrote the paragraphs on the Freer and National Gallery presentations (Part III, Chapter 8).

Bibliography

Arago, François, "The History of My Youth," *Annual Report of the Board of Regents, Smithsonian Institution, Year 1870.* Government Printing Office, Washington, D.C., 1871.

Beaudant, F. S., *Traité Élémentaire de Minéralogie,* Verdière, Paris, 1832.

Burney, Frances, *Diary and Letters of Madame d'Arblay,* edited by Charlotte Barrett. Macmillan & Co., London, 1904–5.

Dana, Edward Salisbury, *A Text-Book of Mineralogy,* J. Wiley & Sons, New York, 1906.

Dawson, Warren R., Ed., *The Banks Letters,* A Calendar of the Mss. Correspondence of Sir Joseph Banks, British Museum (Natural History), 1958.

Goode, George Brown, Ed., *The Smithsonian Institution 1846–1896,* The History of Its First Half Century (includes Langley paper). Smithsonian Institution, Washington, D.C., 1897.

Hayes, E. Nelson, *The Smithsonian Satellite-Tracking Program: Its History and Organization,* Smithsonian Institution, Washington, D.C., 1962.

Jones, Dr. Bence, *The Royal Institution,* Its Founder and Its First Professors, Longmans, Green & Co., London, 1871.

Martin, Thomas, *Royal Institution of Great Britain* (revised edition), Longmans, Green & Co., London, 1948.

Oehser, Paul H., *Sons of Science,* The Life of Science Library, Henry Schuman, New York, 1949.

Perthes, C. T., *The Life of Frederick Perthes,* Thomas Constable & Co., Edinburgh, 1857.

Rhees, William J., *James Smithson and His Bequest,* Smithsonian Institution, Washington, D.C., 1880.

Roscoe, William, *The Life of Lorenzo De Medici,* Henry G. Bohn, London, 1846.

Smith, Edward, *The Life of Sir Joseph Banks,* John Lane, The Bodley Head, London, 1911.

Sollman, Torald Hermann, *A Manual of Pharmacology and Its Applications to Therapeutics and Toxicology*, W. B. Saunders Co., Philadelphia and London, 1934.

Tilloch, Alexander, *The Philosophical Magazine*, Volume XXIX, Printed for John Murray, London, 1808.

Veis, George, *Optical Tracking of Artificial Satellites*, Smithsonian Institution Astrophysical Observatory, Cambridge, Massachusetts.

Wilson, George, *The Life of the Honorable Henry Cavendish*, Printed for the Cavendish Society, London, 1851.

Also Annual Reports of the Secretary of the Smithsonian and manifold publications of the various Smithsonian bureaus.

INDEX